Transistor Fundamentals
Volume 2
BASIC TRANSISTOR CIRCUITS

Transistor Fundamentals
Volume 2
BASIC TRANSISTOR CIRCUITS

by

CHARLES A PIKE

With a specially written chapter for
the guidance of the English reader
by W. Oliver (G3XT)

FOULSHAM-SAMS
TECHNICAL BOOKS
Pubished and distributed by
W. FOULSHAM & CO. LTD.,
SLOUGH   BUCKS   ENGLAND

W. FOULSHAM & CO. LTD.

Yeovil Road, Slough, Bucks., England

TRANSISTOR FUNDAMENTALS VOL 2, BASIC TRANSISTOR CIRCUITS

621. 381528

C00189643

0 572—00639—X

Introduction Printed and Made in Great Britain by East Midland Printing Company Limited, King's Lynn. Balance printed in U.S.A.

It is essential that the English reader should read this chapter.

This book explains in simple terms how basic transistor circuits work. The text is illustrated with exceptionally clear diagrams which make the theory quite easy to follow.

Where circuit diagrams are shown, these have been simplified in the interests of clarity. Details which are not really needed to help you in understanding basic principles have been omitted. For example, transistor type-numbers are not specified; and resistor and capacitor values are not stated except where these are called for by the requirements of the explanations in the text.

Therefore these diagrams are purely for instructional purposes and are not intended to be used, even experimentally, as practical designs for actual construction of transistor projects.

Should you wish to try out practical versions of circuits discussed theoretically in these pages, you will find a wide choice of suitable designs, with all component values, transistor types, etc., fully specified, in several other books in the Foulsham-Sams list. One or other of these various titles contain projects covering virtually the whole range of transistor circuits: radio-frequency and audio-frequency amplifiers; oscillators for use in receivers, transmitters, signal-generators and electronic musical instruments; power supplies; switching devices; and even simplified versions of electronic computer circuitry.

Practical experimenting is a valuable part of technical training but projects should be based on suitable designs complete with Parts Lists giving full details of components. (Any attempt, especially by a beginner, to build practical circuits from simplified teaching diagrams such as those in the present volume is likely to result in failure.)

The author points out, in the first chapter, that transistors can be regarded either as conversion devices or as control devices. Possibly the latter approach is freer from snags for the beginner. Conversion is a term that beginners should beware of taking too literally where electronic devices are concerned. It is easy to fall into the error of supposing that a device is actually changing one thing into another (by some sort of scientific magic!) whereas in fact it is merely acting as a means whereby one thing can be made to control another.

Broadly speaking, electronic devices seldom, if ever, change one thing to another in a strictly literal sense. They often appear to do so, because a signal seems to go into the device in one form and come out in another. For instance, electric currents in the form of audio signals go into a loudspeaker, and sound-waves come out. A plausible explanation seems to be that the loudspeaker changes electricity into sound.

If, however, one takes a loudspeaker unit to pieces it becomes quite evident, even to a complete novice, that the commonplace materials with which it is made could not possibly bring about such a miraculous change.

A typical loudspeaker in a small transistor receiver, for instance, will be found on dismantling to consist of little more than a cone of stiff fabric attached to a short paper tube on which is wound a coil of exceedingly fine enamelled copper wire, this assembly being arranged to move within the field of a small permanent magnet. Obviously there is nothing here that could perform such an astonishing feat as turning electricity into sound!

So one has to seek a more accurate explanation, which is that the varying audio currents in the moving coil within the magnetic field cause the cone diaphragm to vibrate and thereby set up sound waves in the air. Complex variations in the electric currents (the audio signals which are a sort of electrical equivalent of speech, music and other sounds) cause corresponding variations in the sound-waves set up by the physical vibration of the speaker-cone.

So, by an electro-mechanical transducer the electricity produces and controls the sound; but both exist separately and simultaneously; one is not literally changed or converted into the other.

Most electronic processes are pretty complex and the task of explaining circuit action in a way that is at once simple, satisfying and accurate is not an easy one. Often one has to use analogies, but these, as the author points out, all have their weaknesses. Terms and phrases can also be misleading unless one defines their meaning very precisely.

Many modern electronic circuits appear to be very complicated; but fortunately even the most complex circuits become fairly easy to understand if you break them up into small pieces and examine one at a time! Even electronic computers are composed of a multitude of comparatively simple basic units, though they combine to form a bewilderingly complicated whole.

So the transistor configurations described in the present book have been dissected into small sections (in Chapter 3) which makes it extremely easy to understand exactly what is meant by rather puzzling terms such as "common emitter". A glance through the simplified diagrams illustrating Chapter 3 will enable you to grasp the principles of the different transistor configurations immediately and remember them easily.

In the process of amplification, a transistor enables a very small signal-current (in the input circuit) to control a much larger one (derived from the power-supply) thus producing a magnified signal (in the output circuit).

You will realize that you are not really getting something for nothing in this process, as the power-supply has to provide the larger current for the output circuit which is controlled by the variations of the smaller current in the input circuit. As the author points out, no power is actually supplied by the transistors.

Amplifiers, oscillators and similar circuits are dependent, therefore, on a power supply from batteries or a suitable mains unit providing a voltage within the maximum rating of the transistors. Exceptionally, the power may come from some less conventional source, such as solar cells.

One should note, however, that it is not strictly correct to say that such an external power-supply unit is essential to the working of *all* transistor or diode or allied solid-state circuits.

There is at least one notable exception, namely the simplest form of detector circuit, comprising only a tuner, a diode detector or possibly a transistor, a pair of headphones, an aerial and an earth-connection. In a strong-signal district, close to a broadcasting station, a simple circuit like this (which is of course a descendant of the crystal sets commonly used in the early days of broadcasting) will give adequate headphone reception with no power-supply in the ordinary sense—only the incoming signal-currents picked up by the aerial.

FET's are among the semiconductors discussed in Chapter 6 on Special Devices. The definition of "transistor" hardly fits field-effect devices and it has been suggested that fet's should be renamed. Be that as it may, their action is certainly closer to that of a valve than that of a typical transistor, as the author points out.

Fet applications are many and various. The present writer finds that the majority of constructional projects designed to use small triode valves can equally well use field-effect semiconductors with little or no alteration to the circuit, except of course in regard to power supplies.

The writer finds an fet easy to use in a simple variable-frequency oscillator; and some other amateur transmitters have praised certain fet vfo's as being the best and most stable arrangements of this kind that they have yet tried.

As this book originates from the United States, a few of the electronic technical terms used in the text may be unfamiliar to some readers who have not previously studied American technical books or articles. The following are some examples: phonograph means record-player or radiogram; schematics are circuit diagrams; grounded means earthed; and vacuum-tube means valve.

Some of the circuits shown in this book are drawn around PNP transistors and some around NPN types. The author explains that the polarity of the power supply must be reversed in changing from PNP to NPN or vice versa. But another point which beginners should bear in mind is the fact that the polarity of certain electrolytic capacitors, which are likely to be found in a practical constructional project (even though they are omitted for the sake of simplicity from the purely instructional diagrams in these pages), will also be affected by reversal of power-supply polarity.

Such capacitors must be connected the right way round to suit the polarity of the power supply and transistors in any given circuit.

ERRATUM

Fig. 5-17 on page 152 of the present edition showing the circuit arrangement of a simple astable multivibrator. At (A) in the sketch a superfluous line joins up the lower ends of resistors R1 and R4, thereby short-circuiting the base and collector of Q2, the second transistor. The redrawn version of the circuit at (B) is free from this error.

Introduction

This volume describes the basic principles of operation of the junction transistor. Semiconductor physics is introduced, but is limited to very simple explanations that are needed to describe the internal workings of the transistor. Emphasis is placed on the transistor as a circuit element. The transistor is basically a current device (as opposed to a voltage device), and the reader is encouraged to think of it as such. The concept of input current regulating or controlling output current in a way the circuit designer desires, is essential to understanding the transistor as a circuit component. The transistor does not actually generate any current itself, but rather controls the current from the power supply.

The discussion on amplifiers and oscillators is aimed to make the basic operation well understood. Simple circuits illustrate the desired points of interest. Once the fundamentals are learned, complicated and sophisticated circuits can be handled with better understanding.

The chapter on recent semiconductor developments describes the basic operation of four devices. A few basic circuits using these devices are included to give some idea of how these components are used.

WHAT YOU WILL LEARN

You will learn the principles underlying the operation of the junction transistor. The book is intended to teach the basic concepts, rather than specific circuits. No attempt is made to enumerate the many applications of the transistor. Circuit examples are given where they will help the reader grasp the idea being presented. When you have finished the book you should have a clear understanding of the operation of the transistor as a circuit element.

WHAT YOU SHOULD KNOW
BEFORE YOU START

Some background in atomic physics is desirable but not necessary. The reader should know the general electrical properties of resistors, capacitors, and inductors, and what functions they perform in circuits. The fact that there has to be a complete path in order to have current is an important idea, as well as the meaning of direct and alternating current. It is assumed the reader knows Ohm's law in its various forms and can apply it to simple situations. Naturally, the more familiar you are with circuit concepts, the easier it will be to follow the description of the transistor as a circuit element. The only math required is that needed to understand and manipulate simple equations.

WHY THE PROGRAMMED TEXT FORMAT
WAS CHOSEN

During the past few years, new concepts of learning have been developed under the common heading of programmed instruction. Although there are arguments for and against each of the several formats or styles of programmed textbooks, the value of programmed instruction itself has been proved to be sound. Most educators now seem to agree that the style of programming should be developed to fit the needs of teaching the particular subject. To help you progress successfully through this volume, a brief explanation of the programmed format follows.

Each chapter is divided into small bits of information presented in a sequence that has proved best for learning purposes. Some of the information bits are very short—a single sentence in some cases. Others may include several paragraphs. The length of each presentation is determined by the nature of the concept being explained and by the knowledge the reader has gained up to that point.

The text is designed around two-page segments. Facing pages include information on one or more concepts, complete with illustrations designed to clarify the word descriptions used. Self-testing questions are included at the end of each of these two-page segments. Most of these questions are in the form of statements requiring that you fill in one or more missing words; other questions are either multiple-choice or simple essay types. Answers are given at the top of the succeeding page, so you will have the opportunity to check the accuracy of your response and verify what you have or have not learned before proceeding. When you find that your answer to a question does not agree with that given, you should restudy the information to determine why your answer was incorrect. As you can see, this method of question-answer programming ensures that you will advance through the text as quickly as you are able to absorb what has been presented.

HOW YOU SHOULD STUDY THIS TEXT

Naturally, good study habits are important. You should set aside a specific time each day to study, in an area where you can concentrate without being disturbed. Select a time when you are at your mental peak, a period when you feel most alert.

Here are a few pointers you will find helpful in getting the most out of this volume.

1. Read each sentence carefully and deliberately. There are no unnecessary words or phrases; each sentence presents or supports a thought which is important to your understanding of the technology.
2. When you are referred to or come to an illustration, stop at the end of the sentence you are reading and study the illustration. Make sure you have a mental picture of its general content. Then continue reading, returning to the illustration each time a detailed examination is required. The drawings were especially planned to reinforce your understanding of the subject.
3. At the bottom of most right-hand pages you will find one or more questions to be answered. Some of these contain "fill-in" blanks. In answering the questions, it is important that you actually do so in writing, either

in the book or on a separate sheet of paper. The psysical act of writing the answers provides greater retention than merely thinking the answer. Writing will not become a chore since most answers are short.

4. Answer all questions in a section before turning the page, to check the accuracy of your responses. Refer to any of the material you have read if you need help. If you do not know the answer, even after a quick review of the related text, finish answering any remaining questions. If the answers to any questions you skipped still have not come to you, turn the page and check the answer section.

5. When you have answered a question incorrectly, return to the appropriate paragraph or page and restudy the material. Knowing the correct answer to a question is less important than understanding why it is correct. Each section of new material is based on previously presented information. If there is a weak link in this chain, the later material will be more difficult to understand.

6. Carefully study the Summary Questions at the end of each chapter. This review will help you gauge your knowledge of the information in the chapter and actually reinforce your knowledge. When you run across questions you do not completely understand, reread the sections relating to these statements, and recheck the questions and answers before going to the next chapter.

7. Complete the final test at the end of the book. This test reviews the complete text and will offer you a chance to find out just what you have learned. It also permits you to discover your weaknesses and initiate your own review of the volume.

This volume has been carefully planned to make the learning process as easy as possible. Naturally, a certain amount of effort on your part is required if you are to obtain maximum benefit from the book. However, if you follow the pointers just given, your efforts will be well rewarded, and you will find that your study will be a pleasant and interesting experience.

Contents

CHAPTER 5

CHAPTER 6

1

Introduction to Basic Concepts

What You Will Learn

Important concepts and ideas concerning transistor circuits and how they operate in conjunction with the input signal and power supply to produce an output signal are discussed in this chapter. You will learn how a transistor circuit can be thought of as a conversion device—converting an input signal to an output signal by means of current supplied by the power supply. A good grasp of basic current paths will help you in understanding the operation of various circuits and provide a good foundation for learning troubleshooting techniques.

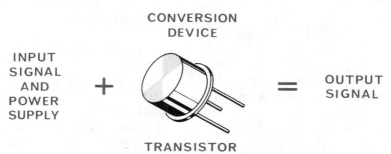

INPUT SIGNAL AND POWER SUPPLY + CONVERSION DEVICE TRANSISTOR = OUTPUT SIGNAL

Fig. 1-1. Transistor is a conversion device.

SYSTEM CONSIDERATIONS

Before we discuss specific individual circuits, the basic elements required to operate a system of circuits will be considered. The discussion is very general and is intended to point out the relationship among the elements.

Basic Elements

The basic elements required for the operation of any electronic system are a source of input signal, a load to absorb the output signal, a power supply, and the circuits that perform various functions to attain the desired output signal. Fig. 1-2 illustrates these elements. This book is concerned with the transistor circuits that perform various functions within the system. The power supply, source of input signal, and output load are pretty much taken for granted in most of the discussions throughout the book.

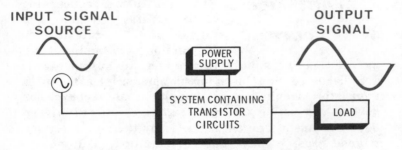

Fig. 1-2. Basic elements of an electronic system.

However, when you are actually troubleshooting a piece of equipment, the first thing to check is the power supply and input signal. Do not take them for granted when a system is not operating properly.

The basic elements shown in Fig. 1-2 apply for all sizes and types of systems. A television set, a phonograph, and a radio receiver all have input-output signals, a power supply, and circuits that perform various functions. Even a very large scale digital computer, with thousands of transistors, can be broken into subsystems, each having input-output signals. Regardless of the size of a system, its operation can usually be understood by breaking the system down into smaller subsystems. If this reducing process is continued, eventually a single stage is reached with its own input-output signals. This book will develop the theory of operation of the transistor using a single stage in the explanation. It should be no trouble, theoretically at least, to connect these individual circuits together to form a system. Note that when this is done the output signal of one circuit becomes the input signal of the next circuit.

It is a good practice to learn as much as possible about the characteristics of the input-output signals. Many things can be learned about the nature of the circuits just by comparing the output signal to the input signal. For instance, in Fig. 1-2, the output signal is shown as an enlarged version of the input signal. Circuits that affect the input signal in this manner are called amplifiers. The answer to how this output signal got to be an enlarged version of the input signal by passing through the circuits is at the very heart of the basic operation of the transistor. The reader is encouraged to approach the learning of any transistor circuit with the input and output signals in mind.

The actual interconnection of the basic elements is developed in the next section of this volume. It is very important that the reader has a good grasp of how the basic elements mentioned in this section operate together. Once the fundamentals are understood, the size of any piece of equipment should present no extra problems in understanding its operation.

Q1-1. The first item to be checked when a piece of equipment is not operating properly is the ___PoweR___ ___SuPPLy___, since it is the source of current for all circuits.

Q1-2. Is it necessarily true that the larger a system is, the more complicated and complex the individual circuits will be? Why?

Q1-3. A system whose output signal is much larger than its input signal is called a (an) ___AMPLIFIER___.

Transistor as a Control Device

The transistor is the component in a circuit that controls the current through the various other components. Fig. 1-3 shows the interconnection between the basic elements introduced in the previous section. It is by no means a working circuit, but rather a diagram to show the basic current paths between the system elements.

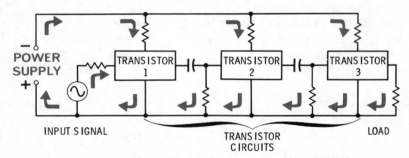

Fig. 1-3. Basic current paths between system elements.

Current Control—The methods of controlling the current through the various transistor circuits is covered in the next chapter. For now the important point to note is that except for the input signal, all current is initially supplied by the power supply. Each transistor regulates or controls the amount of current through it from the power supply.

By controlling the current through itself, the transistor also controls the current through various resistors and other components in the circuit. In this way, the desired voltages can be established at different points in the circuit, and functions such as amplification are achieved. The transistor can be thought of as being a conversion device—converting the current supplied by the power supply into the desired output current under the control of an input current.

The currents shown in the illustration are from one terminal of the power supply, through the various transistor stages and load, and back to the other terminal of the power supply, thus making a complete path. The polarity indicated at the terminals of the power supply means that the direction of the arrows is the direction of electron flow. This convention is adopted throughout this book.

From the interconnection shown in the diagram, you can see that the input signal flows into transistor 1 to draw a certain amount of current from the power supply and develop the signal that becomes the input signal to transistor 2. This cause and effect relationship continues until the last transistor delivers the desired signal into the load. The discussion in the next section will help you to further understand these basic ideas.

Q1-4. The transistor converts the ___INPUT___ supplied by the power supply into the desired output current.

Q1-5. Electrons flow away from the ___NEGATIVE___ terminal of the power supply toward the ___POSITIVE___ terminal.

Input Signal—The signal that serves as the input for a transistor is current. It may be argued that since current is the result of a voltage applied across a resistance, cannot the input therefore be considered a voltage. However, it is better to adopt the current concept. Not only does the physics of transistor operation lend itself to the current concept, but it will be seen to be more practical when discussing circuit operation.

Fig. 1-4 shows a few typical sources of input current. A television or radio antenna intercepts an electromagnetic field and develops a current to drive the first stage of the receiver. The cartridge in a phonograph arm produces a current that is the input to the circuits. These are examples of input currents from external sources feeding a system.

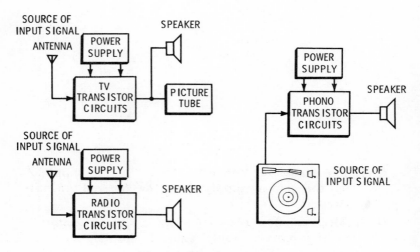

Fig. 1-4. Sample systems.

Output Signal—The development of a desired output signal is the reason for having a system in the first place. The drawing shows that the circuits in a phonograph or radio are used to provide an output signal to a speaker. Television circuits not only provide a signal to the speaker but also have to develop signals for the picture tube. The output currents supplied to the loads actually come from the power supply. The output transistor stage controls or regulates this current. In most cases within a system of circuits, the output current of one stage actually becomes the input current to the next stage.

Power Supply—All the power dissipated in the system and delivered to the load is supplied by the power supply. This follows from the previously mentioned fact that all the current is supplied by the power supply. No power is actually supplied by the transistors.

This book will not cover the design of power supplies. Instead, the assumption will be made that the necessary supply of current is available at the voltage required. In most cases the power supply will be represented by a pair of terminals marked + and −. This does not detract from the discussion of the circuits in any way.

Q1-6. **Match the numbered items on the left with the most appropriate items on the right. Not all lettered items are used:**

1. **Power supply**
2. **Load current**
3. **Transistor circuit**
4. **Input current**
5. **Amplifier**

A. **Controlled by output transistor**
B. **Supplies all current used in system**
C. **Requires no external power supply**
D. **Output signal enlarged reproduction of input signal**
E. **Originally supplied by output transistor**
F. **Regulates current drawn by transistor**
G. **Current - conversion device**

TRANSISTOR AS AN ACTIVE DEVICE

This section will show the differences between the most common passive device, the resistor, and the transistor (which is an active device) as far as the control of current is concerned. In this way, the idea of the transistor as a conversion device will be better understood.

Assume that a battery is placed across a resistor as shown in Fig. 1-5A. According to Ohm's law, a certain amount of current will be present. This current depends on the values of E and R. Assuming that E and R are fixed, I is constant.

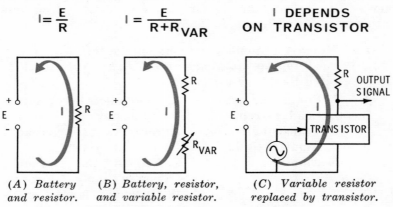

$$I = \frac{E}{R} \qquad\qquad I = \frac{E}{R+R_{VAR}} \qquad\qquad \begin{array}{c} I \text{ DEPENDS} \\ \text{ON TRANSISTOR} \end{array}$$

(A) Battery and resistor.   (B) Battery, resistor, and variable resistor.   (C) Variable resistor replaced by transistor.

Fig. 1-5. Transistor as a control device.

If a variable resistor were placed in series with the original one, then the circuit would be as shown in Fig. 1-5B. The current is now dependent on E, R and R_{var}. By varying the resistance of R_{var}, we could vary the current through R and R_{var}, and thus the voltage at the junction of R and R_{var} would vary accordingly.

20

The next step is to replace the variable resistor with a transistor. The circuit now appears as shown in Fig. 1-5C. Instead of a variable resistor regulating the current, a transistor is now used. Instead of manually adjusting a variable resistor to attain the desired voltage (suggested only for the purpose of discussion), an input signal can be applied to the transistor which will vary the current through R and through the transistor. The current will vary according to the input signal, just as the current in Fig. 1-5B varied according to the manual adjustments of the variable resistor. The voltage at the junction of R and the transistor will vary in accordance with the current. This voltage is the output signal.

A few important points should be emphasized. The transistor is not simply a variable resistor. This analogy (and all analogies have weaknesses) was used only to illustrate that the transistor, under the command of an input signal, controls or regulates current through a circuit. Note that the current labeled I, which develops the output signal, is supplied by the power supply—not by the transistor. Note also that the current labeled input signal does not appear in the output circuit. The input signal "tells" the transistor how much current to allow in the output circuit. Thus the transistor is a conversion device—converting an input signal into an output signal, using the current supplied by the power supply. A good grasp of this basic concept will help in understanding the operation of various circuits in subsequent chapters.

Q1-7. In the analogy presented in Fig. 1-5, the __INPUT__ __CURRENT__ of Fig. 1-5C takes the place of manually adjusting the variable resistor and the __TRANSISTOR__ takes the place of the variable resistor itself.

Q1-8. The current is not supplied by the transistor but is __CONVERTED__ by the transistor.

Q1-9. The transistor can be thought of as a (an) __ACTIVE__ device.

Q1-10. The transistor transforms a (an) __INPUT__ signal into a (an) __OUTPUT__ signal by means of current supplied by the power supply.

Your Answers Should Be:

A1-7. In the analogy presented in Fig. 1-5, the **input signal** of Fig. 1-5C takes the place of manually adjusting the variable resistor, and the **transistor** takes the place of the variable resistor itself.

A1-8. The current is not supplied by the transistor, but is **regulated** by the transistor.

A1-9. The transistor can be thought of as a **conversion** device.

A1-10. The transistor converts an **input** signal into an **output** signal by means of current supplied by the power supply.

BRIEF PREVIEW OF VOLUME CONTENT

Throughout the book, you will proceed from an understanding of some simple concepts to more practical applications. Since the operation of the transistor depends on the physics of semiconductors, a discussion sufficient for understanding this operation is presented. When actually studying circuits, the internal physical happenings usually give way to thinking of the currents in and out of the transistor. The discussion of the physics is important however, when indicating the various electrical limitations and ratings of the transistor.

After the semiconductor discussion, the "how" of transistor operation is given. Basic current paths are described so the reader is ready to study the three circuit configurations. These basic circuit configurations are developed in detail, and characteristic curves and operating limits are explained. Following the basic circuits the various classes of amplifiers are discussed with various coupling networks introduced.

Chapters 5 and 6 deal with circuits other than amplifiers. Various oscillators are described and analyzed. Pulse and switching circuits are covered and semiconductor devices other than the transistor are considered, along with their circuit uses.

SUMMARY QUESTIONS

1. This chapter has introduced the transistor as a conversion device. The basic elements of input-output signal, the circuit itself, and the power supply were introduced. A transistor circuit converts or transforms an input signal into an output signal by means of current supplied from a power source. It should be emphasized that the transistor itself does not supply any current or power, but rather regulates or controls the current supplied by the power supply.

   a. The basic function of the transistor is to control or regulate the ___CURRENT___ supplied by the ___POWER___ ___SUPPLY___.

   b. By its conversion action, the transistor produces a (an) ___OUTPUT___ signal from a (an) ___INPUT___ signal.

2. To help further an understanding of the transistor as a conversion device, an analogy was made between the transistor and a variable resistor. This analogy showed that just as current can be controlled by manually varying the value of a resistor, current can also be controlled by the transistor under the influence of the input signal.

   a. It is impossible to operate without a (an) ___INPUT___ ___SIGNAL___, since a transistor cannot generate its own power.

SUMMARY ANSWERS

1a. The basic function of the transistor is to control or regulate the **current** supplied by the **power supply**.

1b. By its conversion action, the transistor produces an **output** signal from an **input** signal.

2a. It is impossible for a transistor to operate without a **power supply**, since a transistor cannot generate its own power.

2

Transistor Principles

What You Will Learn

To understand the internal conduction mechanism of the transistor, an elementary knowledge of the structure of matter is required. In particular, the subject of semiconductors should be understood. This chapter begins with a review of the structure of matter and semiconductor principles. You will learn how other substances are added to semiconductor materials to form a crystal capable of being used as a diode or transistor. N- and P-type semiconductor materials will be discussed. By utilizing the properties of a junction made between an N-type and P-type material, a semiconductor diode is formed.

The theory of a single P-N junction is extended to the use of two junctions to form a transistor. You will learn how sections of P-type and N-type material form the transistor crystal. Classification of transistors according to the arrangement of the P- and N-type material is explained. What is happening inside the transistor to allow current through it is described.

After the explanation of the internal workings of the transistor, you will be introduced to the transistor as a circuit element. You will learn how the transistor is connected to a power source and other elements, such as resistors and capacitors, to form a working circuit.

SEMICONDUCTOR PHYSICS

Transistors are constructed from materials called semi-conductors. Before embarking on the subject of semiconductors, a very brief review of atomic structure is given. This review will help introduce semiconductors and their relationship to other materials.

Atomic Structure Review

The world of matter is made of atoms. Everything around us is made up of an organized collection of atoms. Atoms contain three fundamental particles called electrons, protons, and neutrons. The easiest way to picture the atom is to think of it as having a center core called the nucleus with particles called electrons whirling about this nucleus in orbits or shells. This is shown in Fig. 2-1. It should be mentioned that this is only a very elementary picture which is adequate for our purposes but would have to be modified by the findings of modern physics to be technically correct.

Nucleus—The central core of the atom, called the nucleus, consists of several different kinds of particles. The two most important are called protons and neutrons. Protons carry a positive charge of one unit; neutrons carry no electrical charge. Protons and neutrons are each about 1800 times heavier than electrons.

Electrons—Electrons are negatively charged particles whirling around the nucleus at fantastic speeds. They are

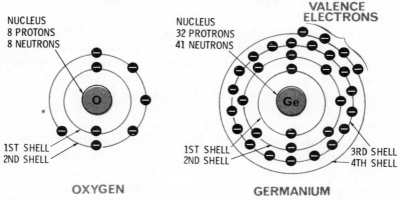

Fig. 2-1. Oxygen and germanium atoms.

arranged in orbits or shells. Each of these shells can hold a specific number of electrons. The innermost shell can hold two electrons, the second shell can hold eight, the third shell can hold eighteen, and so on. The shells are filled starting with the inner shell and working out so that when the inner shells are filled with as many electrons as they can hold, the next shell is started. The electron and the proton have equal amounts of opposite charge; the electron is a negatively charged particle and the proton is a positively charged particle. There are as many electrons as there are protons in a given atom, which leaves the entire atom electrically neutral.

Valence Electrons—Most elements do not have a completed outer shell—that is, they do not have the maximum allowable electrons in their outer shells. These outer electrons are called valence electrons. They contribute to the material's electrical and chemical properties. These incomplete outer shells make the atom active in that it can combine with other atoms.

Three types of atomic bonds are created by the valence electrons. They are ionic, metallic, and covalent bonds. These bonds determine the conductivity of the material. An example of an ionic bond is sodium chloride—table salt.

The metallic bond exists in good conductors of electric current. In this type of bond the valence electron is loosely bound to its atom and is free to move among the various atoms.

The covalent bond is characteristic of crystals. Each atom shares its valence electrons with other atoms forming an orderly network called a lattice structure. Since semiconductors have this type of bond it will be discussed further in the next section when the structure of the germanium crystal is considered.

Q2-1. Two important particles in the nucleus of an atom are the _____ and _____.

Q2-2. _____ are negatively charged particles that whirl around the _____ in discrete orbits.

Q2-3. The electrons in the outer shell which determine the electrical and chemical properties of a material are called _____ electrons.

Conductivity of Materials

Conductivity is a measure of the ability of a material to conduct electric current. All materials may be classified as either conductors, insulators, or semiconductors.

Good conductors are those materials that have a large number of free electrons. In general, all metals are conductors of electricity. As shown in Fig. 2-2, copper, aluminum, and silver are metals that are commonly used as conductors.

Insulators are materials that have an atomic structure such that the movement of electrons is very limited. Thus, they do not conduct current very easily. No material is a perfect insulator, but for all practical purposes, many are classified as insulators. Some examples of common insulators are glass, wood and mica.

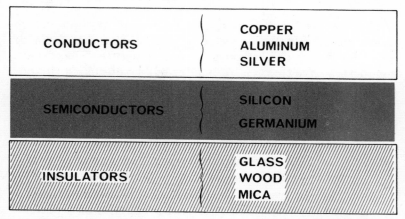

Fig. 2-2. Examples of a conductor, insulator, and semiconductor.

Between the categories of conductors and insulators are some materials classified as semiconductors. These materials are neither good conductors nor good insulators, but exhibit partial conductivity. Two semiconductor materials that are of particular interest, because they are used for transistors, are germanium and silicon. The covalent bonds among the atoms in pure germanium are shown in Fig. 2-3. Only the valence electrons are shown. Note how adjacent atoms share electrons. These electrons are bound in place and do not readily contribute to electrical conduction. The question now arises as to how such a material can be used in transistors where current is essential. The answer to this question is given in the next section.

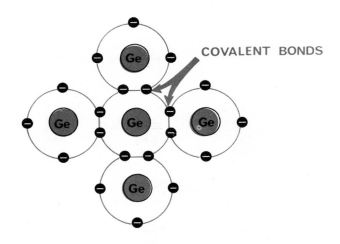

ONLY VALENCE ELECTRONS SHOWN

Fig. 2-3. Covalent bonds among germanium atoms.

Q2-4. The ability of a material to conduct electric current is called the _____ of the material.

Q2-5. Which material has a higher conductivity, copper or mica?

Q2-6. Semiconductors such as germanium and silicon are characterized by the _____ bonds that tightly hold the valence electrons to the atoms.

Semiconductors

As discussed in the previous section, the electrons in pure germanium are bound in place and do not readily contribute to electric current. However, if sufficient energy is applied, a covalent bond may be broken and an electron freed. This applied energy may be in the form of heat.

Hole Generation—When the electron leaves the bond and becomes free, a so-called hole is left in its place. This chain of events is depicted in Fig. 2-4. The hole that was created tries to find another electron to pair with and to fill the hole.

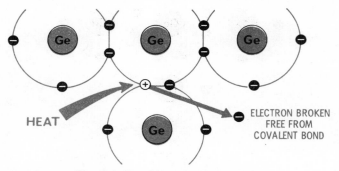

HEAT

ELECTRON BROKEN FREE FROM COVALENT BOND

Fig. 2-4. Breaking covalent bonds.

It does this by stealing another electron from an adjacent atom. This fills the original hole, but a new hole is formed where this stolen electron was. Since the hole is an absence of a negatively charged electron, it is thought of as a positively charged quantity. In a transistor, the creation of a hole is not brought about by heat energy, but rather by substituting some of the germanium atoms with atoms of other materials. These added atoms are called impurities and the process of adding them to the pure semiconductor material is called doping.

Impurities Added—Fig. 2-4 shows how a hole can be formed in a semiconductor by the application of heat. However, for a germanium transistor, holes are generated by substituting a very small number of atoms of a material that has only three valence electrons for some of the germanium atoms. Fig. 2-5A shows an indium atom in place of one germanium atom. The three indium valence electrons have entered into covalent bonds with adjacent germanium atoms, but this leaves one adjacent germanium atom with an electron that is not bonded with another electron. This absence of an electron corresponds to the presence of a hole. This type of material is called a P type.

Just as a hole was generated by adding an impurity, a surplus electron can be developed by adding in place of a germanium atom an atom with five valence electrons. An element such as arsenic could be used. Fig. 2-5B shows an arsenic atom in place of a germanium atom. This type of material is called N-type material.

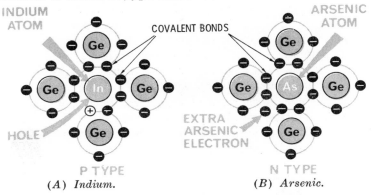

(A) *Indium.*   (B) *Arsenic.*

Fig. 2-5. Impurities added.

Q2-7. **The process of adding impurities to a pure semiconductor material is called** _____.

Q2-8. **Substituting indium for a germanium atom develops a (an)** _____.

Q2-9. **Substituting arsenic for a germanium atom develops a** _____ _____.

P-Type Material

P-type material is formed when atoms of an element with three valence electrons take the place of a number of ger-manium atoms as shown in Fig. 2-6A. A P-type material is represented by plus signs enclosed in circles, as shown in Fig. 2-6B. P-type material will support conduction of an electric current by motion of the positive hole. This can be remembered by relating the p in positive to the P type.

Majority and Minority Carriers—If a battery is con-nected to the ends of a slab of P-type material, current will occur due to hole motion. The holes would move toward the negative terminal of the battery. This hole motion is really a reaction movement. It is caused by the desire of electrons in the doped semiconductor material to enter into covalent bonds. Once a hole has been formed, it moves from atom to atom as different electrons enter into covalent bonds. The majority current carriers in P-type material are holes, but some conduction is also due to free electron movement. Therefore, the electrons that contribute to conduction in P-type material are called the minority carriers.

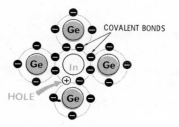

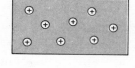

(A) *Formation.*   (B) *Schematic representation.*

Fig. 2-6. P-type material.

N-Type Material

When impurity atoms having five valence electrons are added to germanium, N-type material is formed, as shown in Fig. 2-7A. The addition of this type of impurity atom to the germanium results in covalent bonds formed between four valence electrons of the impurity atom and the surrounding germanium atoms. The fifth valence electron of the impurity atom cannot enter into a covalent bond, since there are no adjacent electrons available. N-type material is represented schematically by minus signs enclosed in circles, as shown in Fig. 2-7B. Conduction is by means of electron flow in N-type material. This can be remembered by relating the *n* in negative to the *N* type (electron has a negative charge). The majority carriers of electric current in N-type material are electrons. Holes are called the minority carriers.

Acceptors and Donors—The impurities added to form P-type material are called *acceptors*. The impurities added to form N-type material are called *donors*.

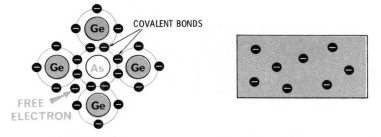

(A) *Formation.*   (B) *Schematic representation.*

Fig. 2-7. N-type material.

Q2-10. To form P-type material from pure germanium, an impurity with _____ valence electrons is necessary.

Q2-11. The majority current carriers in P-type material are _____.

Q2-12. Why is N-type material represented schematically by minus signs enclosed in circles?

Q2-13. Impurities added to P-type material are called _____.

P-N JUNCTION

When P- and N-type germanium are fused together, the point at which they join is called the junction. Fig. 2-8 shows the initial status existing in the N- and P-type materials after they have been joined. The majority and minority carriers are identified for each type of material.

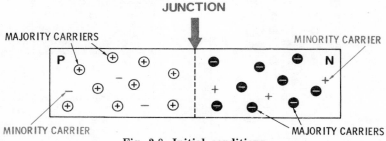

Fig. 2-8. Initial conditions.

There is no applied electric field, but the holes and electrons are in a random movement called *diffusion*. The holes and electrons are evenly distributed through both types of material. It may be expected that the holes and electrons would diffuse across the junction, combine and eliminate all holes and excess electrons. However, a very important phenomenon occurs at the surface where contact is made between the two types of material.

Junction Barrier

Majority carrier electrons (free electrons) in the N-type material near the junction are just as likely to cross the boundary into the P region as to move further into the N region. Likewise, holes are likely to diffuse from the P region into the N region. When this starts to happen, these migrating electrons and holes will recombine close to the junction. The electrons that have entered into combination with holes have left behind positively charged atoms. This results in a situation as depicted in Fig. 2-9. The plus signs in the N region near the junction are the positively charged atoms which lost their free electron. The minus signs in the P region are the negatively charged atoms which had their holes filled with electrons. This region is known as the *depletion* region, because there is a depletion, or lack of holes and electrons in this area. The important thing to note is that any additional electrons that would diffuse from the N region to the P region are repelled by the negatively charged atoms. For this reason, the electric field created by the charged atoms (called ions) in the depletion region is called a *barrier*. This phenomenon should be well understood since it is at the heart of transistor operation.

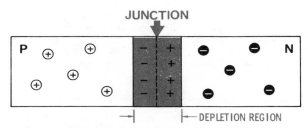

Fig. 2-9. Results of migration and recombination.

Q2-14. Why do the free electrons from the N-type material, that enter into bonds with holes near the junction, leave behind positively charged atoms?

Q2-15. In the P side of the depletion region, the polarity of the charged atoms contributing to the junction barrier is _____.

Reverse Bias

When an external battery is connected to a P-N junction, as shown in Fig. 2-10, with the positive terminal connected to the N region and the negative terminal to the P region, the junction is said to be reverse biased. Holes in the P region are attracted to the negative terminal away from the junction. Electrons in the N region are attracted to the positive terminal of the battery away from the junction.

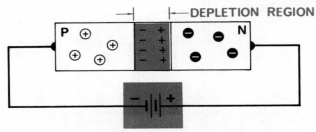

Fig. 2-10. Reverse-biased P-N junction.

Thus, both types of majority carriers move away from the barrier, leaving behind more charged atoms to add to the junction barrier. This continues until the barrier charge equals the potential of the external battery, then the current stops. This condition is conventionally called reverse bias or back bias because it offers maximum resistance to an external flow of majority carriers.

Forward Bias

If the battery connections in Fig. 2-10 are reversed, the junction will be forward biased. This is shown in Fig. 2-11. The plus terminal repels the holes in the P region toward the junction, and the negative terminal repels the electrons in the N region toward the junction. Some of these holes and electrons enter into the depletion region and combine. When this happens, an electron enters the N-type material from the external wire under the influence of the battery. Likewise, a hole is created in the P-type material

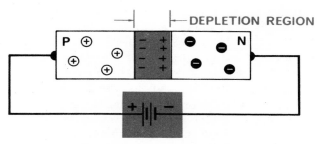

Fig. 2-11. Forward-biased P-N junction.

by an electron breaking a covalent bond and entering the positive terminal of the battery. Under the influence of the external battery, holes and electrons continue to recombine in the depletion region and electrons flow in the external circuit. This condition is known as forward-biasing the junction. A P-N junction that is forward biased conducts current, while a junction that is reverse biased does not.

Q2-16. A P-N junction is reverse biased when the _____ terminal of the battery is connected to the P material, and the _____ terminal is connected to the N material.

Q2-17. Even though part of the internal conduction mechanism of a forward-biased junction is by means of holes, is it true that all the current in the external wires is by electron flow?

Semiconductor Diode

The ability of the P-N junction to conduct in one direction and not in the other makes it suitable for use in circuits as a diode. Fig. 2-12 compares the voltage-current relationship between a resistor and a diode. For a resistor, as the voltage is increased in either direction, the current will increase proportionately. This is shown in Fig. 2-12A. For a diode, in the forward direction current increases for an increase in voltage, but not in the same proportion. Fig. 2-12B shows that a point is reached in the forward direction where just a small increase in voltage gives a large increase in current. In the reverse-bias direction, there is no current as the voltage is increased until so-called avalanche breakdown occurs, when the current increases rapidly.

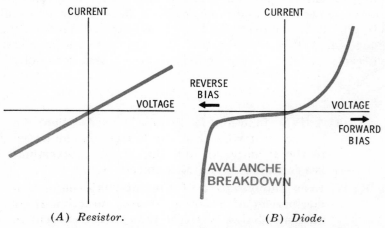

(A) Resistor.   *(B) Diode.*

Fig. 2-12. Curves of voltage versus current.

Rectification—One of the most important circuit functions of the diode is rectification. This is the process of converting an alternating voltage (one that continuously changes its polarity or direction) to a voltage that has only one direction or polarity. It is able to do this because it conducts current for only one of the polarities of the alternating voltage.

Symbol—Until now in our discussion, the semiconductor diode has been represented as shown in Fig. 2-13A. When drawing circuit schematics, however, the symbol for the diode is shown as in Fig. 2-13B. This symbol will be used from now on to represent a diode in a circuit schematic.

Before extending the theory of the P-N junction to the transistor, a word should be mentioned about the percentage of impurity atoms that are added with respect to the germanium atoms. A very small amount, in the order of 1 impurity atom to 10^8 germanium atoms, is all that is required to produce diode action. Varying the amount of impurity doping has important results, as will be discussed later.

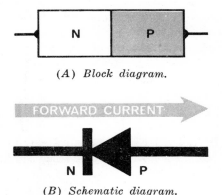

(A) *Block diagram.*

(B) *Schematic diagram.*

Fig. 2-13. Diode symbol.

Q2-18. The P-N junction has the properties of a diode. It conducts current easily when _____ biased, and does not conduct when _____ biased.

Q2-19. Draw a battery and diode (using schematic symbol) connected so the diode is forward biased.

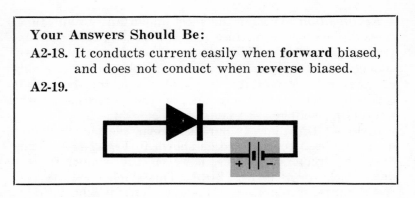
HOW TRANSISTORS OPERATE

The study of semiconductor diodes has provided the foundation for understanding the operation of transistors. The explanation of the internal workings of the transistor will be based on the discussion of the forward- and reverse-biased P-N junctins. The transistor consists of two P-N junctions—one forward biased, the other reverse biased. The two junctions share one section so that the transistor actually consists of three sections. Fig. 2-14 shows the two different types of transistors, the NPN and PNP. They are so classified because of the arrangements of the N- and P-type materials. The NPN has a slice of P-type material between two N types, while the PNP has a slice of N-type material between two P types.

Since the majority and minority current carriers are different for the two types of materials, the internal operations of the NPN and PNP transistors are different in this respect. The two types will be discussed separately in the next few sections. Some additional information concerning the P-N junction will be given as the theory of transistor operation is developed.

Fig. 2-14. Two types of transistors.

NPN Transistor

Recall that the NPN transistor has two junctions, one that is forward biased and one that is reverse biased. Our discussion will begin by considering the forward biased junction, as shown in Fig. 2-15. Previously, no mention was made concerning the relative amounts of impurities in the materials forming the junction. However, for the NPN transistor, the N material on one side of the forward-biased junction has more impurity atoms (is more heavily doped) than the P material. This means more current will be carried across the junction by the majority carrier electrons from the N material than by the majority carrier holes from the P type. This imbalance is not important in explaining diode operation, but it is significant in transistors. The point to remember is that in the NPN transistor, the forward-biased junction is so doped that conduction through the junction is mainly by majority carrier electrons from the N-type material.

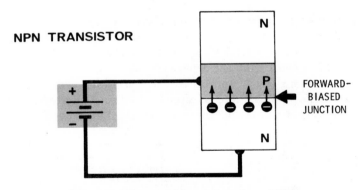

NPN TRANSISTOR

FORWARD–
BIASED
JUNCTION

Fig. 2-15. Forward-biased junction—NPN.

Q2-20. Two types of transistors, classified by the arrangement of the N- and P-type materials, are the _____ and _____.

Q2-21. By doping the _____ material more heavily than the _____ material, current through the forward-biased junction of the NPN transistor is mainly due to _____ movement.

Reverse-Biased Junction—When first discussing the reversed-biased P-N junction, it was said that no current due to majority carriers passed through the junction. However, there is a very small current, called reverse current, due to minority carriers. For the P-N junction, this would be electrons from the P region and holes from the N region. This is shown in Fig. 2-16A. Applying this to the NPN transistor, Fig. 2-16B shows the reverse-biased junction with the reverse current due to electrons from the P material and holes from the N material.

Action of Two Junctions Together—We are now ready to explain the action of the two junctions working together. The explanation will be easier to follow by referring to Fig. 2-17. Recall that the forward-biased junction supplied electrons from the N region to the P region. This was due to the larger percentage of doping in the N material. The P region that these electrons enter is the same P region

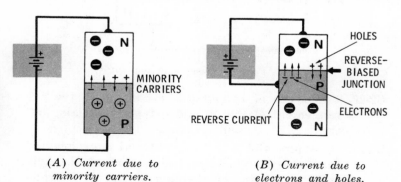

(A) *Current due to minority carriers.*

(B) *Current due to electrons and holes.*

Fig. 2-16. Minority carriers in a reverse-biased junction.

that is part of the reverse-biased junction. Once they are in the P region, these electrons are available to contribute to the minority-carrier current crossing the reverse-biased junction. By controlling the number of electrons crossing the forward-biased junction (by controlling the amount of bias and the percentage of impurity doping), the number of electrons available to contribute to the current passing through the reverse-biased junction is also controlled.

Nearly all the electrons injected into the P region contribute to the current crossing the reverse-biased junction. This is true for two reasons. The first reason is that the P region is very thin compared to the N region, and thus the electrons have little chance of recombining with holes in this region. Secondly, the electrons are under the influence of a higher potential due to the battery supplying the reverse bias and are therefore drawn in that direction.

This discussion of the internal conduction mechanism of the NPN transistor will have more meaning when the transistor is considered as a circuit element in succeeding sections. First, the internal working of the PNP type will be explained.

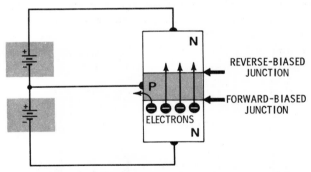

Fig. 2-17. Both junctions working together—NPN.

Q2-22. Conduction through the _____ -biased junction is by minority carrier current.

Q2-23. In the NPN transistor, the _____ region is very thin compared with the _____ regions.

Q2-24. Nearly all the electrons injected into the _____ -type material cross through the reverse-biased junction into the _____ -type region.

PNP Transistor

The theory of operation of the PNP transistor is similar to the NPN except that the majority carriers are holes instead of electrons. The forward-biased junction is shown in Fig. 2-18A. The P region contains many more impurity atoms than the N region, so most of the majority carriers crossing the forward-biased junction are holes. This is in contrast to the NPN transistor where the majority carriers were electrons.

The reverse-biased junction for the PNP transistor is shown in Fig. 2-18B. Recall that the current through this junction is a reverse current made up of minority carriers. For the PNP, this would be holes flowing from the N region and electrons from the P region. The carriers across this junction that are important to transistor action are the holes.

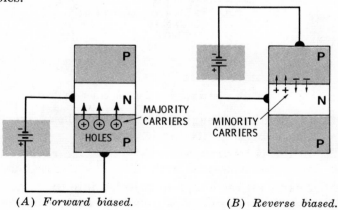

(A) *Forward biased.*   (B) *Reverse biased.*

Fig. 2-18. PNP junctions.

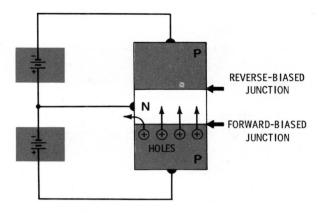

Fig. 2-19. Both junctions working together—PNP.

Action of Two Junctions Together—The action of the forward-biased junction and the reverse-biased junction operating together is similar to the action in the NPN transistor. In the case of the PNP, the forward-biased junction injects holes into the N region (Fig. 2-19). Once the holes are in this N region they are available to contribute to the reverse current through the reverse-biased junction. Because the battery connected to the reverse-biased diode is of higher potential than the battery across the forward-biased junction, the holes that have been injected into the N region are attracted through the reverse-biased junction. Just as in the NPN transistor, the middle section is very thin compared to the two end sections. This is so designed to prevent recombination of the holes with electrons in this middle section.

The internal conduction mechanism of the NPN and PNP transistors has been described. The various currents introduced will now be related to other circuit elements and the transistor's function in a circuit will be discussed.

Q2-25. The majority carriers across the forward-biased junction in the PNP transistor are _____.

Q2-26. The N region is thin compared to the P regions to lessen the probability of holes _____ with electrons in the N region.

Transistor Symbols

The NPN and PNP transistors are identified on schematics by the symbols shown in Fig. 2-20. The three regions comprising the transistor are called the collector, base, and emitter. The forward-biased junction is the base-emitter junction, while the reverse-biased junction is the base-collector junction. The emitter region is so called because it emits majority carriers into the base region. The collector gets its name because it collects the majority carriers from the base region. The base region is so called because it is a support or base for the emitter and collector materials. From now on, the schematic symbols and the terms emitter, base, and collector will be used instead of referring to the forward- and reverse-biased junctions.

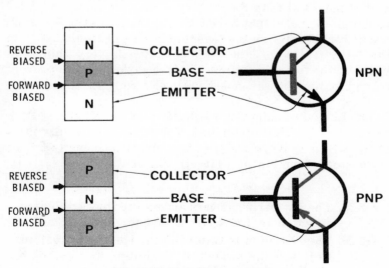

Fig. 2-20. Transistor symbols.

Current—The direction of electron flow in the wires connected to the transistor is shown in Fig. 2-21. For the case of the NPN transistor where electrons are the majority carriers, the electron flow shown is a continuation of the internal flow. For the PNP, the majority current carriers are holes and the internal conduction is due to hole current.

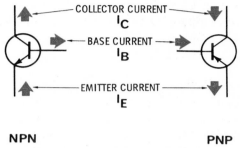

NPN   **PNP**

Fig. 2-21. Electron flow.

However, hole conduction takes place only within the semiconductor crystal itself. This internal hole conduction leads to electron flow in the external wires connected to the semiconductor material. The direction of the electron flow is opposite to the internal hole conduction and it is electron direction that is indicated for the PNP transistor.

Most of the interest from now on will be concerned with the base, emitter, and collector currents indicated in the illustration. Descriptions of the function of the transistor in various circuits will be in terms of these currents.

Q2-27. The base-collector junction is _____ biased.

Q2-28. The base-emitter junction is _____ biased.

Q2-29. The arrowhead on the emitter lead for the _____-type transistor points toward the base region.

Q2-30. For both the NPN and PNP transistors, electron flow is (in the same direction as, opposite to) the direction of the emitter arrowhead.

47

Basic Current Paths

The previous sections furnished the concepts of the P-N junction diode and transistor electron flow. In this section complete current paths will be traced out and some simple relationships concerning emitter, base, and collector currents will be developed.

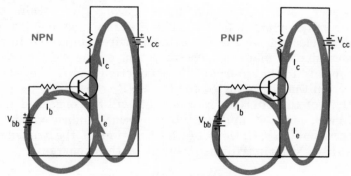

Fig. 2-22. Basic current paths.

Fig. 2-22 shows the basic current paths for the NPN and PNP transistors. The battery labeled V_{bb} provides the forward bias for the base-emitter junction. Forward biasing causes current from one terminal of the battery through the junction and resistor, and back to the other battery terminal. This current is called base current. The resistor is included in this path to indicate that some means of controlling this current is necessary. Recall that most of the majority carriers that are injected into the base region from the emitter do not continue in the base-emitter path. They are attracted

48

toward the larger potential applied to the collector region. This potential is supplied by the battery marked V_{cc}. This current that is attracted to the V_{cc} battery is called collector current. Since both the base current and collector current come from the emitter region, a simple relationship exists between the currents:

$$I_b + I_c = I_e$$

In words this means that the emitter current separates in the transistor into the base current and also the collector current.

The point made in Chapter 1 that the transistor is a conversion device can now be better understood. The amount of collector current depends on the amount of base current. The more base current, the more majority carriers are injected into the base region and the collector current is larger. The base current converts the current supplied by V_{cc} into a controlled current, namely the collector current. The amount of collector current is related to the base current by the following simple but important relationship:

$$\beta I_b = I_c$$

The Greek letter β (Beta) represents the current gain of the transistor.

It is important to understand the twin loop concept depicted in the preceding illustration. One loop is the base-current path and the other loop the collector-current path. As will be seen in the next chapter, the signal to be amplified is added to the base-bias current and the output signal is derived from the collector current. The idea of base current regulating or controlling collector current is basic to the operation of the transistor as an amplifier.

Q2-31. The potential applied to the _____ is larger than the base potential.

Q2-32. Emitter current is the sum of _____ current and _____ current.

Q2-33. Draw in the batteries (and mark polarities) to make the PNP transistor conduct current.

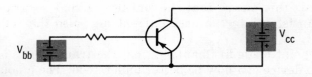
Temperature Effects

The most important temperature consideration is the increase in base to collector reverse current that occurs as temperature increases. Recall that the reverse-biased base to collector junction has a very small current through it due to minority carriers. This situation is shown for the NPN transistor in Fig. 2-23. This current is referred to as I_{co}, short for collector cutoff current. This is the collector current that would flow if the emitter lead were left disconnected. I_{co} has a particular value at room temperature, but it increases as the temperature increases. The situation then exists where there is a certain amount of collector current which is not controlled by the base current, leading to unpredictable results. Precautions that are taken to minimize the I_{co} problem are mentioned when the transistor amplifier is considered.

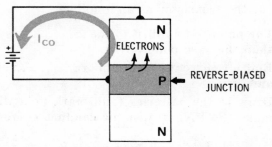

Fig. 2-23. Collector cutoff current (I_{co}).

50

SUMMARY QUESTIONS

1. All matter is made up of atoms. Atoms consist of a central nucleus with electrons whirling about it. Of particular interest for transistor work are the semiconductor materials such as germanium and silicon. The germanium or silicon atoms are bound together in a symmetrical crystalline lattice network. The valence electrons of one atom form covalent bonds with the adjacent atoms. The semiconductor material is made suitable for transistor action by adding impurity atoms, which create either free electrons or holes. A hole can be considered a positive charge. The material that has free electrons is called N-type material, while the material that contains holes is called P-type material.

   a. Characteristic of germanium, the valence electrons of one atom form _____ bonds with the adjacent atoms.

   b. N-type material contains free _____, while P type material has an abundance of _____.

2. A P-N junction is formed when an N-type material and P-type material are joined together. This junction has the characteristic of passing current easily when forward biased, but allowing only a very small current to pass when reverse biased. The forward current is due to majority carriers (holes in P-type and electrons in N-type) while the reverse current is a result of minority carriers (electrons in P-type and holes in N-type).

   a. _____ bias of P-N junction causes heavy conduction while _____ bias causes very low current.

3. Transistors consist of two P-N junctions that share one common region. One type of transistor is the NPN; the other type is the PNP. Holes constitute the main current in the PNP type, while electrons make up the main current in the NPN type. The center region of a transistor is called the base.

   a. The main current in NPN-type transistor is by _____ conduction, while in the PNP type it is by _____ conduction.

   b. The three regions of the transistor are labeled the base, _____, and _____.

SUMMARY ANSWERS

1a. Characteristic of germanium, the valence electrons of one atom form **covalent** bonds with the adjacent atoms.

1b. N-type material contains free **electrons**, while P-type material has an abundance of **holes**.

2a. **Forward** bias of a P-N junction causes heavy conduction while **reverse** bias causes very low current.

3a. The main current in an NPN-type transistor is by **electron** conduction, while in the PNP type it is by **hole** conduction.

3b. The three regions of the transistor are labeled the base, **emitter,** and **collector.**

3

Configurations

What You
Will Learn

This chapter will introduce the reader to the three basic circuit configurations—the common-emitter, the common-base, and the common-collector circuits. You will learn why they are given these names and thus be able to recognize each type when seen in a circuit schematic. Current and voltage relationships between input and output signals will be discussed. The transistor is treated as a circuit element, which is more useful for our purpose than the internal workings learned in the previous chapter.

The advantages of each of the three basic configurations are discussed. Comparison among some typical characteristics of the three configurations is made, and circuits are indicated that make use of different characteristics. Amplifier principles are introduced by analyzing how the transistor circuit converts an input signal into an output signal.

An introduction is made in this chapter to the construction and interpretation of characteristic curves. The curves are useful when a graphical analysis of amplification is desired. The use of the curves is detailed in Chapter 4.

Some operating limits of transistors are covered in this chapter. Such topics as power dissipation, cutoff frequency, saturation voltage and maximum collector current are discussed.

CIRCUIT ELEMENT

The previous chapter explained the internal workings of the transistor. This involved an introduction to semiconductor physics. Such terms as minority and majority carriers, depletion region, donor and acceptor material, and junction barrier were used. One junction of the transistor was said to be forward biased and the other junction reverse biased. This explanation was needed to understand what it is inside the transistor that provides the means for current.

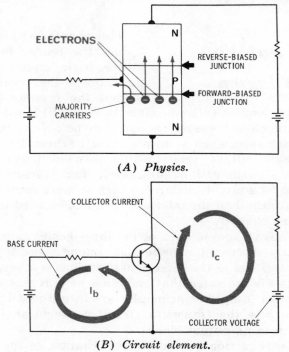

(A) Physics.

(B) Circuit element.

Fig. 3-1. From semiconductor physics to circuit element.

The action of the carriers at a junction should be well understood because the transistor is, in effect, two P-N junctions. If the physical structure of the junction is changed, a variety of interesting results can be achieved. However, to understand the overall operation of a transistor circuit, it is necessary to consider the currents into and out of the transistor and through various components in the circuit.

The input circuit of a transistor is associated with the injection of carriers into the base region. The output circuit is associated with the flow of carriers from the emitter to the collector. The larger portion of the current is between the emitter and the collector, and only a small current will exist between emitter and base. Fig. 3-1 indicates the change in thinking from the internal working aspect to the circuit element aspect.

From now on, the transistor will be drawn as shown in Fig. 3-1B, instead of as shown in Fig. 3-1A. Rather than thinking of majority and minority carriers crossing P-N junctions and holes and electrons moving from atom to atom, we will now think in terms of external current paths. In particular, paths such as those shown for I_b (base current) and I_c (collector current) are of prime interest. The operation of a car provides an analogy. At one time or another, most mechanically minded people learn about the internal workings of the engine, the function of the carburetor, valves, pistons, rings, etc. This corresponds to learning the internal conduction mechanism of the transistor. However, when operating the car, the driver uses the controls in the car without concerning himself too much about what is happening internally. This corresponds to applying a power supply and signal source to a transistor and looking for the desired result without necessarily thinking about the holes and electrons crossing the P-N junctions. Although the explanations of circuit operation given in the next few chapters is not in terms of the internal conduction mechanism, this knowledge should provide a measure of confidence and the reader might profit by reviewing Chapter 2 periodically.

Q3-1. Label the emitter, collector, and base in the illustration.

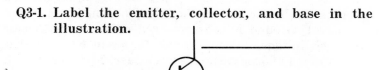

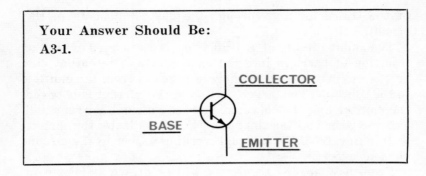
CIRCUIT CONFIGURATIONS

There are three basic configurations for transistor circuits. The three configurations are called the common-emitter, the common-base, and the common-collector circuit. Before discussing the characteristics of each type, an explanation of the names given to these configurations is in order.

Common Element

The input signal to a transistor is applied between two elements. The output signal is taken between two elements. Since there are only three elements in a transistor, one of the elements has to be part of both the input and output circuits. The type of configuration derives its name from the element that is common to both the input and output.

Common Emitter

The most widely used transistor circuit is the common emitter. It is called this because the emitter is common to both the input and output circuits. This is shown in Fig. 3-2. Fig. 3-2A shows the input circuit and Fig. 3-2B shows the output circuit. An important point should be mentioned concerning the illustration in Fig. 3-2. The emitter is shown as grounded. Ground is the reference point in the circuit from which voltages are measured. Notice in Fig. 3-3 that both the input and output signals are measured or referenced to ground. This reference point is called ground because quite often it is connected to the actual earth or ground. Because the common element, the emitter in this case, is

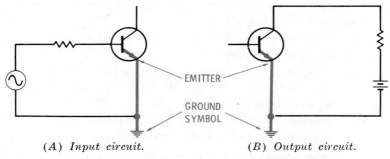

(A) Input circuit.   *(B) Output circuit.*

Fig. 3-2. Common-emitter input and output circuits.

grounded this circuit is sometimes referred to as a grounded-emitter circuit. Common emitter or grounded emitter refer to the same type of circuit. The drawing shows a common emitter stage. Fig. 3-3 does not show all the components usually needed for a working circuit, but is intended to show that the emitter is common to both the input and output.

The example used in this section is for the NPN-type transistor. Everything would still be valid for the PNP type, except the power-supply polarity would be reversed.

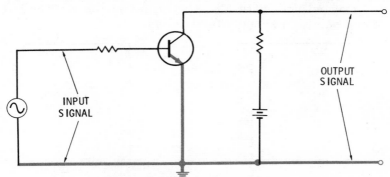

Fig. 3-3. Common-emitter stage.

Q3-2. The most widely used transistor circuit is called the common _____.

Q3-3. The common-emitter circuit is so called because the _____ is common to both the _____ signal and the _____ signal.

Q3-4. Another popular name for the common-emitter stage is the _____ emitter.

Common Base

Fig. 3-4 shows the common-base configuration. The input signal is applied to the emitter-base circuit and the output signal is extracted from the collector-base circuit. Thus, the base of the transistor is the common element. As was the case for the common emitter, Fig. 3-4 is only intended to show why this circuit is called the common base and does not represent a complete working circuit. An NPN transistor is illustrated, but the same circuit applies to a PNP transistor except that the polarity of the power supply would be reversed and, naturally, the arrow on the emitter lead would point in the opposite direction.

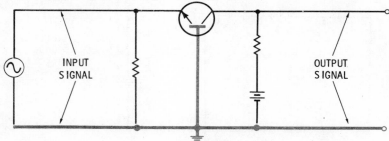

INPUT SIGNAL

OUTPUT SIGNAL

Fig. 3-4. Common-base stage.

Common Collector

The third and final type of configuration is called the common collector and it is illustrated in Fig. 3-5. The input signal is applied between the base and collector, and the output signal is taken between the emitter and collector. Fig. 3-5A is how the circuit is normally drawn, but it doesn't clearly illustrate why it is called a common collector. The

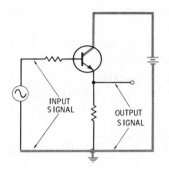 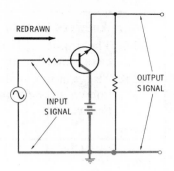

(A) *Normal appearance.*   (B) *Redrawn.*

Fig. 3-5. Common-collector stage.

identical circuit is redrawn in Fig. 3-5B. The transistor has been turned around and this shows clearly that the collector is common to both the input and output signals (the power supply is considered a short circuit to the input and output signals).

As for the other two configurations, another name for the common collector is the grounded collector. However, the most popular name for this circuit is the emitter follower.

Q3-5. The input and output signals of the grounded-base amplifier are referenced to the _____ element.

Q3-6. The common-collector circuit is also popularly known as a grounded _____ or a (an) _____ follower.

Q3-7. Complete the table below by filling in the two elements that the input signal is applied to and the two elements from which the output signal is derived. For example, the output signal in the common-base configuration is taken between the collector and base.

Circuit	Input Signal	Output Signal
common emitter		
common base		collector-base
common collector		

COMMON EMITTER

The first configuration to be discussed in detail is the common-emitter circuit. This is the most popular and versatile of the three types. The best way to arrive at a clear understanding of the performance of the common emitter is to start with the basic concept and add ideas bit by bit until a working circuit is attained.

Basic Concept

Recall from Chapter 2 that in order for a transistor to conduct, the base to emitter junction is forward biased and the base to collector junction is reverse biased. This will cause a base current which in turn results in a collector current (Fig. 3-6). They are related by the expression $I_c = \beta I_b$, where β is the current gain. The first step then is to establish a forward biased base to emitter junction and cause some base current. This is done by connecting the base to a power supply through a resistor to establish the desired current. This is shown in Fig. 3-7A. To provide a reverse base to collector junction and a path for collector current, the collector is returned to a power supply through a resistor (Fig. 3-7B). The two currents together are shown

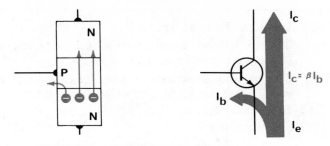

Fig. 3-6. Base-collector current.

in Fig. 3-7C. The same power supply is used for both currents. The process of establishing a base current and a collector voltage is called biasing the transistor. So far only biasing current has been established and no mention has been made of the signal to be amplified.

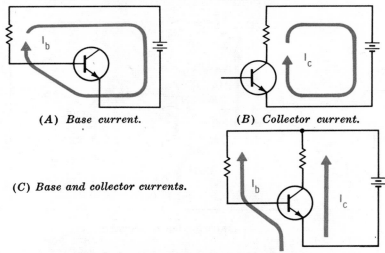

(A) Base current.

(B) Collector current.

(C) Base and collector currents.

Fig. 3-7. Common-emitter biasing.

Q3-8. The important equation relating base current and collector current is _____.

Q3-9. The common emitter is biased by establishing a certain _____ current and _____ voltage.

Q3-10. In the expression $I_c = \beta I_b$, the term β denotes the _____ _____.

Signal Amplification

The signal to be amplified is superimposed or added to the base-bias current. It is introduced into the circuit by means of a capacitor, as shown in Fig. 3-8. This capacitor is called a coupling capacitor because it couples or joins the input signal to the circuit. A capacitor is used because it

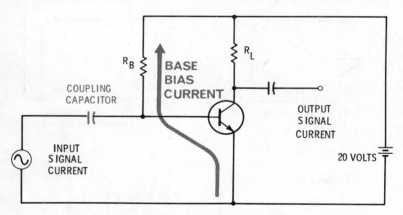

Fig. 3-8. Introduction of signal.

blocks the base-bias direct current from flowing into the source of the signal and yet lets the signal flow into the circuit.

The collector current is β times the base current. β can be looked up in the specifications for the particular type transistor used. Whatever the base current is, β times that current will flow in the collector circuit (assuming linear operation to be explained later). A simple numerical example will help to illustrate these ideas.

Assume we are given the following data:

$\beta = 50$ from transistor specifications

$R_L = 5000$ ohms   determined by load requirements

It is desirable that when no signal current is present, the collector is midway between its minimum and maximum possible operating excursion. In this case, that would be +10 volts since the power-supply voltage is 20 volts. This means that with no signal current we want a 10-volt drop across the 5000-ohm resistor. The desired collector current is then:

$$I_c = \frac{10 \text{ volts}}{5000 \text{ ohms}} = .002 \text{ ampere} = 2 \text{ ma}$$

(ma is the abbreviation for milliampere $= 10^{-3}$ ampere)

If we want 2 ma of collector current, then the required base current can be calculated:

$$I_c = \beta I_b$$
$$I_b = \frac{I_c}{\beta} = \frac{2\text{ma}}{50} = .04 \text{ ma} = 40 \text{ }\mu\text{amps}$$

(μamp is the abbreviation for microampere $= 10^{-6}$ ampere)

To achieve this desired base current, the appropriate value resistor is placed from the base to the power supply. Assuming that there is a negligible voltage drop from base to emitter, the value of base resistor to use to achieve the desired 40 μamps base current can be calculated:

$$R_B = \frac{E}{I_b} \text{ or } R_B = \frac{20 \text{ volts}}{40 \text{ }\mu\text{amps}} = 50,000 \text{ ohms}$$

This common-emitter stage is now biased at 40 μamps base current, 2 ma collector current, and 10 volts collector voltage. We are now ready to introduce the input-signal current into the base and see what happens in the collector circuit.

Q3-11. The _____ capacitor joins the input signal to the amplifier circuit.

Q3-12. The abbreviation for milliampere is _____, which equals _____ ampere.

Q3-13. The abbreviation for microampere is _____, which equals _____ ampere.

Input-Signal Current Applied—An input-signal current is now superimposed on the base-bias current. Assume it is an alternating sine wave that first flows 10 μamps in one direction and then 10 μamps in the other. This is shown in Fig. 3-9A. Such a signal might come from an antenna, microphone, or another circuit. This current will add to or subtract from the base-bias current depending on which direction it is flowing at that instant of time. This is shown in Fig. 3-9B. The total base current is no longer just 40 μamp, but it now varies between 30 μamp and 50 μamp.

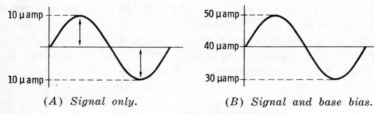

| (A) *Signal only.* | (B) *Signal and base bias.* |

Fig. 3-9. Input-signal current.

The total collector current will vary accordingly. When the base current is 30 μamp, the collector current will be 50 times that or 1.5 ma; and, when the base current is 50 μamp the collector current is 2.5 ma. Thus, we have an amplifier. The base current varied by 10 μamp in each direction and the collector current varied by 500 μamp. This is shown in Fig. 3-10. The varying collector current goes through the load resistor and develops the output voltage. This is covered in the next section on phase reversal.

Note at this time that the output current (collector current) is actually supplied by the power supply, and the

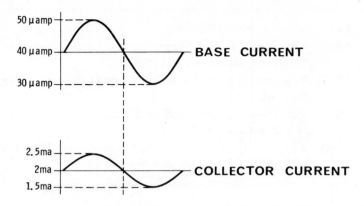

Fig. 3-10. Base current and collector current.

transistor regulates or governs this current under the influence of the base current. The reader should not forget this important concept.

The common-emitter circuit just analyzed is not a very practical circuit. The biasing technique described may work well at room temperatures, but it usually becomes inoperative at higher temperatures. Also β varies from one transistor to another (even of the same type) and a more practical biasing arrangement can be used to compensate for this. In Chapter 4, the common emitter will again be studied and a more practical circuit presented. However, the circuit just described should give the reader good insight into the principles of amplification, using the common-emitter configuration.

Q3-14. The input-signal current adds to or subtracts from the _____ bias current.

Q3-15. The varying base current causes the _____ current to vary.

Q3-16. The base current and collector current are (in phase, out of phase) with each other.

Q3-17. The output current (collector current) is actually supplied by the _____ _____.

Phase Reversal–Common Emitter

The common-emitter circuit is said to provide a phase reversal because the output voltage is 180 degrees out of phase with the input voltage. This will now be explained with the aid of the next two illustrations.

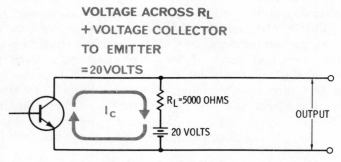

Fig. 3-11. Output circuit.

Referring to Fig. 3-11, notice that as I_c increases, the voltage drop across R_L increases. Since at any one time the voltage drop across R_L and the transistor (from collector to emitter) must equal 20 volts, the voltage from collector to emitter must be decreasing. Likewise, when the voltage drop across R_L is decreasing due to a decrease in I_c, the voltage across the transistor is increasing. Thus, the actual output voltage which is taken from the collector to emitter is 180 degrees out of phase with the collector current. Since the collector current is in phase with the base voltage, the output voltage is also 180 degrees out of phase with the input base voltage. This is what is called a phase reversal. The various relationships are illustrated in the curves of Fig. 3-12. The common-emitter circuit is the only one of the three configurations to give a phase reversal.

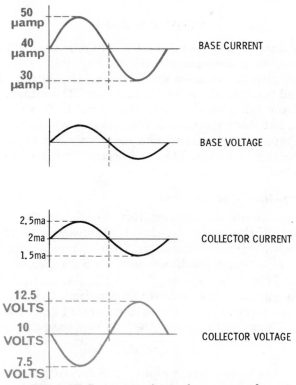

Fig. 3-12. Common-emitter phase reversal.

Q3-18. The common emitter configuration has a phase-reversal because the _____ voltage is 180 degrees out of phase with the input _____ voltage.

Your Answer Should Be:

A3-18. The common emitter configuration has a phase reversal because the **collector** voltage is 180 degrees out of phase with the input **base** voltage.

COMMON BASE

The common- or grounded-base configuration will now be discussed. As previously mentioned, the input signal is applied between the emitter and base and the output signal is extracted between the collector and base. The internal workings of the transistor remain the same as in the common emitter, but since the base is the common element, different things happen to the input and output signals than happen in the common emitter. This will become evident in the next few sections.

Common-Base Current Paths

Just as in the common-emitter circuit, in the common-base circuit the emitter current divides inside the transistor, with a large percentage ($\sim 95\%$) going to the collector and a very small amount ($\sim 5\%$) becoming base current. This is shown in Fig. 3-13. Recall that for the common emitter, the important equation $I_c = \beta I_b$ related the input current (I_b) to the output current (I_c). An equally important equation arises in the common-base configuration

$$I_c = \alpha I_e$$

where α, the Greek letter alpha, is referred to as the common-base current gain. Since about 95% of the emitter current develops into collector current, α generally has values in the .950 region.

Since the output current (I_c) is less than the input current (I_e) the question arises, how is this circuit used as an amplifier? The answer is that it cannot be used as a current amplifier, but by selecting the proper values for the input and load resistor a voltage gain may be attained.

Fig. 3-14 shows the emitter current, collector current, and the two currents together. Just as in the common-

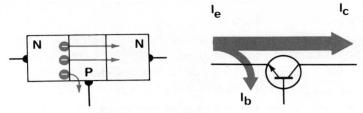

Fig. 3-13. Common-base currents.

emitter circuit, a particular bias condition is achieved by proper choice of biasing resistors. The current paths shown in the illustration should be understood, since the signal currents will be superimposed on them as described in the next section.

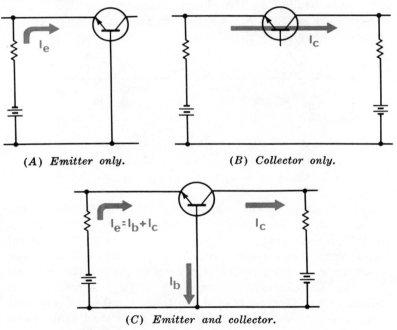

(A) Emitter only.

(B) Collector only.

(C) Emitter and collector.

Fig. 3-14. Emitter and collector currents.

Q3-19. In the common-base configuration, the collector current equals α times the _____ current.

Q3-20. The common-base configuration (does, does not) make a good current amplifier.

Introduction of Signal

Assume that resistor values have been calculated to give the desired bias currents. The procedure would be similar to that used in the common-emitter example. However, for the common-base amplifier, the input signal is superimposed or added on to the emitter current rather than on the base current as it was in the common-emitter circuit. This is shown in Fig. 3-15 where the signal to be amplified is capacitor-coupled to the circuit.

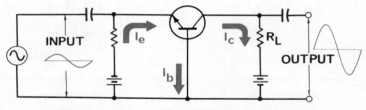

Fig. 3-15. Signal added to bias currents.

The drawing of the waveforms (Fig. 3-16) shows the phase relationships among the voltage and current at the input, and the voltage and current at the output. As the input signal voltage increases, the emitter current will decrease. Since the collector current is related to the emitter current by $I_c = \alpha I_e$, it also will decrease. The voltage across R_L will increase as I_c decreases, so the output signal increases. The reverse occurs as the input voltage decreases. Note from Fig. 3-16A and D that the input voltage and output voltage are in phase, showing that there is no phase reversal in the common-base configuration. This brief description indicates how the common base can be used as an amplifier, with a more detailed description given in Chapter 4. Before leaving this section, the reader should understand how the common base can provide a voltage amplification even though it cannot provide a current gain.

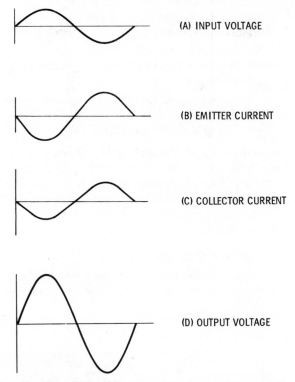

(A) INPUT VOLTAGE

(B) EMITTER CURRENT

(C) COLLECTOR CURRENT

(D) OUTPUT VOLTAGE

Fig. 3-16. Phase relations in the common-base circuit.

Q3-21. In the common-base configuration, the signal current is superimposed or added on to the _____ bias current.

Q3-22. The common-base circuit does not give current gain because the _____ current is less than the _____ current.

71

COMMON COLLECTOR

The fundamentals of the last of the three basic configurations, the common collector, will now be explained. As in the previous two configurations, the NPN transistor will be used in the explanation. The explanation would be the same for the PNP, except the polarity of the power supplies would be reversed.

Common-Collector Current Paths

The common collector currents are shown in Fig. 3-17. These are the same as those shown for the common emitter.

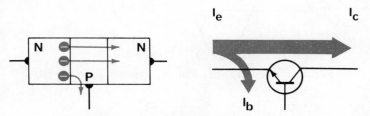

Fig. 3-17. Common-collector currents.

However, the collector, instead of the emitter, is common to input and output, and the load resistor is in the emitter circuit. This makes a difference in the circuit operation of the two configurations. Since the load resistor is in the emitter lead, both the input and output currents pass through this resistor. This is the only configuration where this situation occurs.

Fig. 3-18 shows the biasing currents. Just as in the common emitter, base current is established by connecting the base to a power supply through a resistor. However, in this case, the base current also goes through the resistor in the emitter lead. Collector current appears in this resistor too, and establishes a voltage drop across this resistor in such a direction as to oppose base current. Thus, the base current

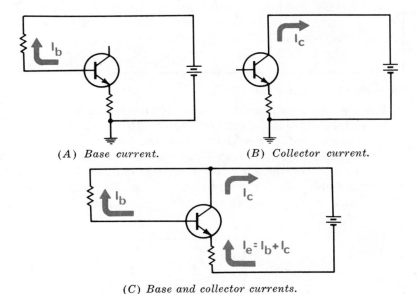

(A) *Base current.*　　　　(B) *Collector current.*

(C) *Base and collector currents.*

Fig. 3-18. Common-collector biasing.

upon which the input signal will be superimposed encounters or sees a large resistance from the base, through the transistor and load resistor, to ground. The fact that the common collector has a high input resistance and low output resistance is one of its most important characteristics.

Q3-23. The current paths for the common collector are the same as for the common ＿＿＿＿＿, with only the common element being changed.

Q3-24. The common collector has a high input resistance because ＿＿＿＿＿ current through the load resistor establishes a voltage drop that opposes the ＿＿＿＿＿ current.

A3-23. The current paths for the common collector are the same as for the common **emitter,** with only the common element being changed.

A3-24. The common collector has a high input resistance because **collector** current through the load resistor establishes a voltage drop that opposes the **base** current.

Introduction of Signal

The signal to be amplified is capacitively coupled to the base and is extracted between the emitter and collector. This is illustrated in Fig. 3-19. Since the base to emitter is forward biased, there is very little voltage drop across this junction, and the output voltage at the emitter is almost the same amplitude as the input base signal. For this reason this circuit is most popularly called an emitter follower.

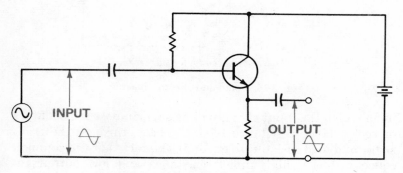

Fig. 3-19. Signal added to bias currents.

The emitter (output) follows the base (input). Thus, there is no voltage gain and the common collector is most commonly used to couple a high-resistance output to a low-resistance load. This will be covered in the next section where the three configurations are compared.

Fig. 3-20 shows the phase relationship between input and output signals. Note that the input voltage and output voltage are in phase.

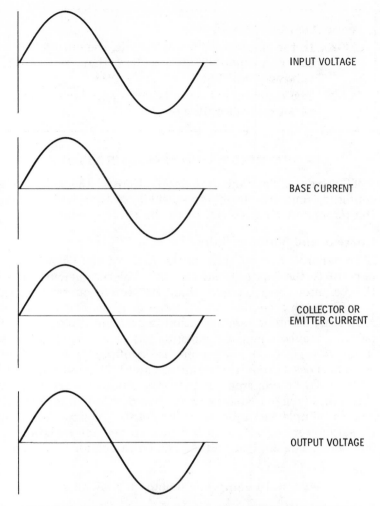

INPUT VOLTAGE

BASE CURRENT

COLLECTOR OR
EMITTER CURRENT

OUTPUT VOLTAGE

Fig. 3-20. Phase relations in the common-collector circuit.

Q3-25. In the common-collector circuit, the output voltage amplitude is always (more, less) than the input voltage amplitude.

Q3-26. The common collector is more popularly known as a (an) _____ _____.

COMPARISON OF CONFIGURATIONS

Thus far, a fundamental description of the three basic configurations has been given. This section will compare the important characteristics of the three configurations.

Current and Voltage Gain

In general, current gain is the ratio of the output signal current to the input signal current. The output current for the common base is less than the input current (recall $I_c < I_e$) so this configuration actually gives a current loss. However, a voltage amplification is possible. Voltage amplification occurs when the output voltage is larger than the input voltage. In the common-base configuration, the input current goes through a small resistor. Thus, the collector current, although smaller than the emitter current, goes through a larger resistance and thus develops a larger voltage. A simple example will show this. Assume an input signal current of 10 μamp through an emitter resistance of 500 ohms. The emitter voltage can be calculated:

$$V_e = I_e R_e$$
$$= 10 \ \mu\text{amp} \times 500 \ \text{ohms} = .005 \ \text{volts}$$

Since approximately .98 of the emitter current is in the collector circuit, the collector signal current will be 9.8 μamp. Assuming a collector resistance of 250,000 ohms, the collector voltage will be:

$$V_c = I_c R_c$$
$$= 9.8 \ \mu\text{amp} \times 250,000 \ \text{ohms} = 2.45 \ \text{volts}$$

Thus, the voltage gain is $2.45 \div .005 = 490$. A voltage gain has been attained even though there is a current loss.

The common-emitter circuit gives both a current gain and a voltage gain. For this reason it is by far the most versatile and widely used configuration. Recall the relationship $I_c = \beta I_b$, where β is the common-emitter current gain and generally has values between 30 and 100. This current gain comes about by the very nature of the internal workings of the transistor. A voltage gain is realized because the collector current (output) goes through a larger resistor than the base current (input). For example, if 10 μamp of base signal current goes through a 1000-ohm input resistance, the input voltage is .01 volt. Assuming a β of 50, the collector current is 500 μamp. A typical collector resistor might be 10,000 ohms, so the output voltage is 500 μamp $\times$ 10,000 ohms, or 5 volts. The voltage gain is $5 \div .01 = 500$.

The common collector is different from the common base in that it can produce a current gain, but it has a voltage gain less than one. The current gain for the common collector is almost the same as that for the common emitter. This is because the input current to both circuits is base current, while the output current for the common collector is emitter current and for the common emitter it is collector current. These two currents are almost equal, making the current gain almost the same. As mentioned before, the voltage gain is less than one. This is because the output is taken off the emitter, which is at a slightly lower voltage than the base. Thus the common collector is used as a current amplifier only.

Q3-27. The common-_____ circuit gives both voltage and current gain.

Q3-28. The common-_____ circuit gives current gain but has less than unity voltage gain.

Q3-29. The common-_____ circuit gives voltage gain but has less than unity current gain.

Your Answers Should Be:

A3-27. The common-**emitter** circuit gives both voltage and current gain.

A3-28. The common-**collector** circuit gives current gain but has less than unity voltage gain.

A3-29. The common-**base** circuit gives voltage gain but has less than unity current gain.

Input and Output Resistance

In general, the input resistance of a transistor circuit can be considered to be the resistance that signal current encounters between the input element and the common element, which is usually grounded. For the common base and common emitter this resistance is usually rather low since the only resistance encountered is the base to emitter forward-biased junction. The input signal in the common-collector circuit encounters not only the forward-biased junction, but the load resistor in the emitter lead as well. As mentioned before, the output current also goes through this resistor and establishes a voltage drop across it that opposes the input current. For this reason the input resistance is quite high for the common collector.

The output resistance can be thought of as being the resistance from the output element "looking back" into the transistor to the common element. The output resistance for the common base is the reverse-biased collector to base junction. This is the highest output resistance of the three configurations. The common-emitter output resistance is lower than the common base because it includes the reverse-biased collector-base junction and forward-biased base-emitter junction. The forward-biased junction provides an internal feedback path that lowers the resistance of the reverse-biased collector-base junction and therefore decreases the whole output resistance. The output resistance of the common-collector circuit is the lowest of the three configurations. Because of its high input resistance and low output resistance, the common-collector circuit is often used to match a high-resistance device, such as a crystal phonograph pickup, to a low-resistance load. Chart 3-1 shows some typical values (for comparison purposes) of the more important characteristics of the three configurations.

Chart 3-1. Comparison of Characteristics of the Three Configurations.

Characteristic	Common Base	Common Emitter	Common Collector
	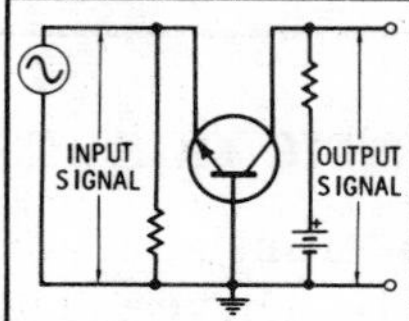	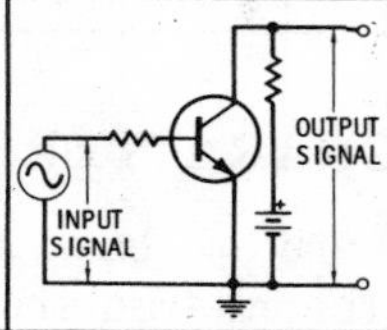	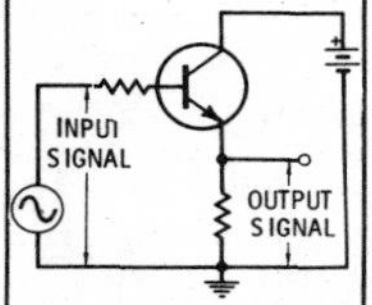
Current Gain	Less Than 1 (.93-.99)	30 to 100	30 to 100
Voltage Gain	500 to 800	300 to 600	Less than 1 ($\approx$ .95)
Input Resistance	50 to 200 Ohms	500 to 1000 Ohms	20,000 to 100,000 Ohms
Output Resistance	$\approx$ 300,000 Ohms	$\approx$ 50,000 Ohms	$\approx$ 500 Ohms
Input-Output Phase	In Phase	180° Out of Phase	In Phase

Q3-30. An input resistance of 100,000 ohms (is, is not) typical for the common-base or common-emitter circuits.

Q3-31. Of the three configurations, the common_____ has the highest input resistance and _____ output resistance.

CHARACTERISTIC CURVES

A clear picture of how a transistor amplifies can be derived from the characteristic curves. These curves are plots of various voltages and currents as other voltages or currents are varied. Two sets of curves are particularly useful. They are the output characteristic curves for the common-emitter and common-base circuits. In this chapter, the construction of the curves will be developed with only an introduction to their usefulness. In Chapter 4, a graphical analysis of an actual amplifier will be made and the real value of the curves will become evident.

Common-Emitter Characteristic Curves

The most widely used family of curves supplied by the transistor manufacturers is the common-emitter output characteristic curves. Fig. 3-21 shows a circuit that can be used to develop the family of curves. The three items of interest are the base current, the collector current, and the collector voltage. Meters are inserted in the circuit to mea-

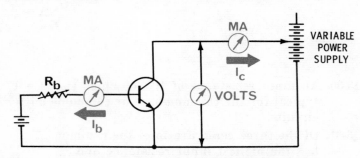

Fig. 3-21. Circuit used for construction of curves.

sure these parameters. The curves are plotted by selecting a particular base current (by adjusting R_b) and increasing the collector voltage while monitoring the collector current.

Fig. 3-22 shows a portion of the family of curves that results from measurements taken for different values of I_b. Start with $I_b = 0$ μamps. Set the collector voltage to 5 volts and measure I_c. This is point ① on the curve. Then set the collector voltage to 10, 15 and 20 volts, measuring

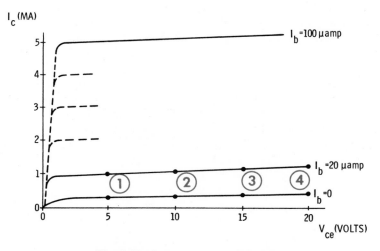

Fig. 3-22. Output curves (partial).

I_c each time. This results in points ②, ③, and ④ on the curve The result of joining these points together is the single curve marked $I_b = 0$. By increasing the base current to say 20 μamp (by adjusting R_b) and again making measurements of I_c as collector voltage is varied will lead to another curve marked $I_b = 20$ μamp. A whole family of curves can be generated this way by selecting convenient values of base current.

Q3-32. The most widely used set of curves is the common-_____ output characteristic curves.

Q3-33. From Fig. 3-22, determine the collector current for a constant $I_b = 20$ μamp as the collector voltage is increased from 5 volts to 20 volts.

Load Line

The previous section described how the output curves are generated. This was done by keeping I_b constant and varying the collector power supply. However, this is done only to construct the curves. The actual use of the curves is quite different.

An important line, called the *load line*, is determined and drawn on the curves. Assume, from the amplifier specifications, that a load resistor, R_L, of 4000 ohms is required. A straight line, called the 4000-ohm line, is shown in Fig. 3-23 and it can be constructed on the family of curves in the following way. The example uses a 20-volt power supply.

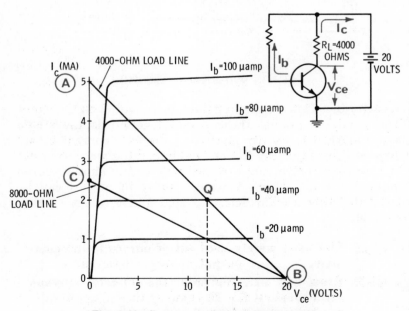

Fig. 3-23. Common-emitter output curves.

The two points used to determine the location of the load line are: (1) when $V_{ce} = 0$ and the full 20 volts are across the 4000-ohm resistor (this makes $I_c = 5$ ma and is marked Ⓐ on the curves), and (2) when $V_{ce} = 20$ volts and there is no current in the collector (this is marked Ⓑ in the curves). The line joining these two points is the 4000-ohm load line.

Note that point Ⓑ is determined solely by the power-supply voltage. If R_L were 8000 ohms, point Ⓑ would be the same as with a 4000-ohm load. However, when $V_{ce} = 0$, I_c would be 2.5 ma and it is shown as point Ⓒ on the curves. The 8000-ohm load line would be the line joining points Ⓑ and Ⓒ.

Once the load line has been drawn on the family of curves, a suitable operating point can be determined. Suppose it is decided to operate somewhere in the middle of the load line at point Q. This is specified by a particular base current (40 μamp) and collector voltage (12 volts). The whole purpose of bias current then is to establish an operating point with no signal in the circuit. This point is called the quiescent point because it is the quiet, still, or no-signal operating point. It is determined solely by the bias conditions. Where to select Q on the curves and what happens when a signal is introduced into the circuit is covered in Chapter 4, where a graphical analysis of amplification using the output characteristic curves is given.

This same set of curves can be used for the common-collector circuit since I_c and I_e are almost the same ($I_c = \alpha I_e$). The only change needed would be to use I_e instead of I_c in the curves shown in the illustration.

Q3-34. The operating point in a circuit with no signal current is called the _____ point.

Q3-35. Assuming an R_L of 8000 ohms, determine from the curves in Fig. 3-23 the approximate value of V_{ce} for $I_b = 40$ μamps.

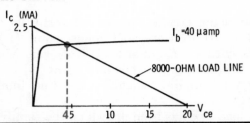

Common-Base Characteristic Curves

To construct the common-base output characteristic curves, a circuit such as the one shown in Fig. 3-24 is used. Meters are placed in the circuit to measure the parameters of interest. For the plotting of the common-base curves, I_e is held constant and the collector current is monitored while the collector supply is varied. For each value of I_e a

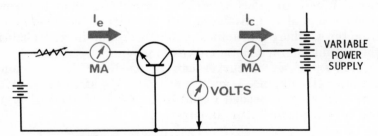

Fig. 3-24. Circuit for common-base curve construction.

single curve is determined. When all these curves for different values of I_e are plotted together, a family of curves such as those shown in Fig. 3-25 results. They look very similar to the common-emitter curves except for one very important point. The so-called "running" parameter in the common-base curves is the emitter current, while in the common emitter it was the base current. These are the input currents to their respective circuits.

The load line for the common base is determined in a similar manner as that used for the common emitter. An example is shown in Fig. 3-25 for a 4000-ohm load resistor. Just as for the common emitter, the operating point with no signal is called the quiescent point and is labeled Q in the figure. Note that the I_e curves have the same value as the value of I_c along the vertical axis. This is as expected since I_e and I_c are approximately equal $(I_c = \alpha I_e)$.

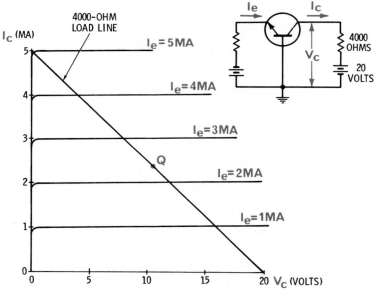

Fig. 3-25. Common-base output curves.

Q3-36. At the Q point on the common-base output curves, the collector current is _____ and the collector voltage is _____.

Q3-37. The common-base output curves show that the collector current (is almost equal to, is β times) the emitter current.

OPERATING LIMITS

Several precautions must be considered in selecting a particular type of transistor for reliable operation in a circuit. The most important limitations are maximum collector voltage and current, maximum power dissipation, and cutoff frequency. A brief discussion on these subjects follows.

Collector Voltage and Current

Just as for other electronic devices, it is reasonable to assume that the voltage and current applied to a transistor cannot be increased indefinitely without damage occurring. The maximum voltage that can be applied between the collector and emitter is limited by a phenomenon called breakdown. The output curves previously shown for the common emitter did not extend in the V_{ce} direction far enough to show the breakdown voltage. Fig. 3-26 shows that if V_{ce} is

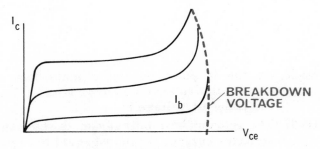

Fig. 3-26. Breakdown voltage.

extended far enough, a sudden increase in collector current occurs even though the base current has been kept constant. The voltage at which the curve breaks sharply upward is called the breakdown voltage. Most transistors have a voltage-breakdown rating of at least 30 volts. Since the transistor does not function normally and is subject to destruction in this region, the quiescent operating point has to be selected so this area is avoided.

Breakdown voltage establishes the maximum allowable voltage. The maximum current, however, is not as well defined. The maximum current allowed really depends on the operating voltage, and the combination of the two establish a maximum power dissipation. This is discussed in the next section. Except in special cases, such as pulse-switching applications, a large collector current is not desirable for another reason besides power dissipation. The higher the collector current, the lower is the current gain. Generally speaking, the particular requirements for establishing the quiescent point will establish the collector current.

Q3-38. Breakdown voltage is accompanied by a sudden (increase/decrease) of collector current.

Q3-39. The breakdown-voltage region can be avoided by properly selecting the _____ operating point.

POWER DISSIPATION

There is a maximum power that the transistor itself can dissipate. If more than this power is dissipated, the transistor will be destroyed. Since power is current times voltage, the maximum allowable power can be plotted on the

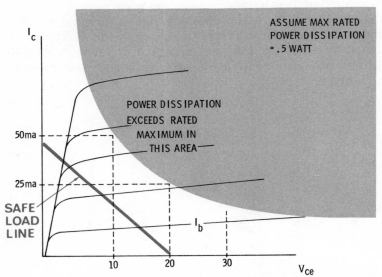

Fig. 3-27. Maximum power dissipation.

collector voltage versus collector current output curves, as shown in Fig. 3-27. If the collector voltage is multiplied by the collector current a curve such as that labeled "maximum allowable power" results. The shaded area is where the power dissipation exceeds the manufacturer's rating. The curve in the illustration is for an assumed maximum rating of .5 watt. The load line and quiescent point should be selected so that at no time do the collector voltage and current result in operating in the shaded area.

Cutoff Frequency

The current gain, α, is usually specified for a low-frequency signal such as 1000 hertz (cycles per second). However, as frequency is increased, α begins to diminish. This is due to transit time of the internal carriers and various capacitances in the transistor. The fall-off of α with frequency is shown in Fig. 3-28. The frequency at which α falls to 0.7 of its value at low frequency is called the cutoff frequency. The example in the figure shows a cutoff frequency of approximately 10 MHz. The transistor still operates beyond this frequency, but the gain will be lower.

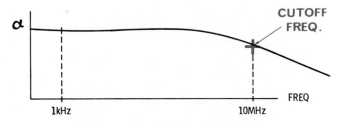

Fig. 3-28. Frequency cutoff.

Q3-40. If the quiescent point of a transistor is at a collector current of 50 ma and a collector voltage of 20 volts, the transistor power dissipation with no signal applied is _____.

Q3-41. The frequency at which α falls to 0.7 of its low frequency value is called the _____ frequency.

SUMMARY QUESTIONS

1. The transistor has three elements: the emitter, the base and the collector. Any of the three elements can serve as the common element for the input and output signals. This leads to the three configurations called the common emitter, common base, and common collector. The three configurations have different characteristics, so the choice of which to use in a particular circuit depends on the circuit requirements.

   a. Sketch the three transistor configurations, indicating the input and output signals.

2. Of the three circuits, the common emitter is the most versatile and used more than the other two. The common-emitter circuit has moderate input and output resistance, high current gain, and a voltage gain. An important equation relating base current and collector current is $I_c = \beta I_b$, where β is the common-emitter current gain. The output-voltage signal is 180 degrees out of phase with the input signal, so the common emitter is said to give a reversal.

   The common-base configuration is characterized by low input resistance, high output resistance, high voltage gain, and a current gain of less than one. An important equation relating collector current and emitter current is $I_c = \alpha I_e$ where α is the common-base current gain. The output-signal voltage is in phase with the input signal so the common-base circuit does not give a phase reversal.

   The common-collector circuit has a high input resistance, low output resistance, high current gain, and a voltage gain of less than one. The output signal is in phase with the input and is at a slightly lower voltage than the input. Since the output "follows" the input and is taken from the emitter element, the common collector is more popularly called an emitter follower.

    a. The common-_____ configuration is the only circuit to give a voltage and current gain of more than unity.

    b. The common-_____ circuit is the only one to give a phase reversal.

    c. The common-_____ is more widely known as an emitter follower.

3. Characteristic curves were introduced in this chapter to lay the foundation for the graphical description of amplification, using the curves, given in the next chapter. Since the common emitter is the most widely used configuration, the common-emitter output curves are usually published in the manufacturer's data sheet. The construction of the curves was explained with the aid of a circuit that could be used to plot the curves. The load line is drawn on the curves and a suitable quiescent point is selected, depending on circuit requirements. Once the point has been selected, biasing resistors can be calculated to achieve the desired bias currents.

    a. The _____ point, located on the _____ line, establishes the operating point of the transistor with no signal applied.

4. Important operating limits were introduced in this chapter. They are maximum collector voltage, collector current and power dissipation, and cutoff frequency. Exceeding the maximum rated collector voltage leads to a condition called breakdown, which could permanently damage the transistor. To exceed the maximum power dissipation would almost certainly destroy the transistor. The cutoff frequency refers to the frequency at which the current gain is 0.7 of what it is at low frequency.

    a. The power dissipation can be calculated by multiplying the collector _____ times the collector _____.

SUMMARY ANSWERS

1a.

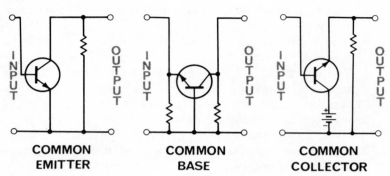

| COMMON EMITTER | COMMON BASE | COMMON COLLECTOR |

2a. The common-**emitter** configuration is the only circuit to give a voltage and current gain of more than unity.

2b. The common-**emitter** circuit is the only one to give a phase reversal.

2c. The common **collector** is more widely known as an emitter follower.

3a. The **quiescent** point, located on the **load** line, establishes the operating point of the transistor with no signal applied.

4a. The power dissipation can be calculated by multiplying the collector **voltage** times the collector **current.**

4

Transistor
Amplifier Circuits

What You

Will Learn

The amplifier princi-
ples introduced in the
previous chapter are ex-
tended in this chapter to
the point where practical,
working circuits are presented. By now the reader
should have firmly established in his mind the basic
concept of amplification. This concept starts with the
application of a signal current to the input circuit of
the amplifier. The transistor enables a current that is
controlled by the signal input current to appear in the
output circuit. The output current is actually supplied
by the power supply.

Basic circuit classes, called class-A, -B and -C amplifiers, are introduced. This classification refers to the
portion of each cycle of the input signal that causes an
output current through the transistor. The discussion
includes a description of the different classes and when
and why they are used. This will lead to a more detailed explanation of transistor biasing. Special emphasis will be placed on the biasing of a class-A amplifier,
with stabilizing as the operating point of particular
interest. All of the explanation thus far has assumed
the presence of a resistor load with a capacitor for
coupling the output current to the next circuit. This is
called an RC network. A number of other coupling
networks are briefly described at the end of this chapter.

CLASSES OF AMPLIFIERS

In previous discussions, it has been assumed that an input current was going into the transistor at all times. This would cause an output current at all times. However, this situation is not always the case. For reasons to be discussed later in the chapter, it may not be desirable to have the transistor conducting for the full cycle of the input signal. The portion of a cycle of the input signal for which there is an output current determines a main classification of amplifiers.

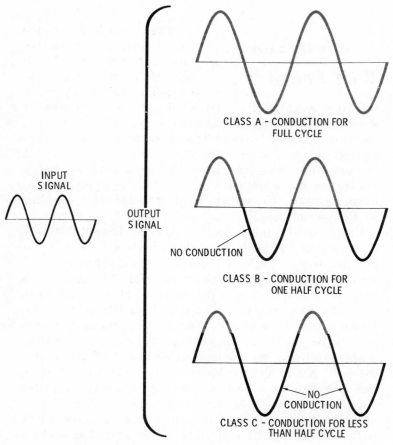

Fig. 4-1. Output signals.

The three main classes are defined as:

Class-A amplifier—the transistor bias and the amplitude of the input signal are such that there is an output current for the full cycle of the input signal. This is the most basic type of amplifier and will receive the largest coverage in this chapter.

Class-B amplifier—the transistor bias and the amplitude of the input signal are such that there is an output current for only half of the cycle of the input signal. The other half of the time no output signal flows through the transistor.

Class-C amplifier—the transistor bias and the amplitude of the input signal are such that there is an output current for appreciably less than one half of each cycle of the input signal.

The definitions of the classes presented above can be illustrated as shown in Fig. 4-1. The drawing shows an input signal with three possible output currents, depending on whether the circuit is biased as a class-A, class-B, or class-C amplifier. The next section will show graphically how the transistor biasing can lead to the three classes of amplifiers.

As in previous discussions of this type, it does not matter whether the transistor is an NPN or a PNP type. The design of a circuit is the same for both types, except for the polarity of the power supply.

Q4-1. The type of amplifier circuit that most closely reproduces the input signal is the class-_____ amplifier.

Q4-2. If a transistor is biased so that there is an output current for only half of each cycle, it is called a class-_____ amplifier.

Graphical Description

To indicate the effect that transistor bias has on the classification of an amplifier, the common-emitter output characteristic curves will be used. Fig. 4-2 shows the curves and the situation for the three classes. The discussion here assumes a resistor load and a coupling capacitor (an RC amplifier). In the more detailed sections on the class-B and class-C amplifiers, it will be seen that this RC network is not very practical for these two classes. The intention here, then, is just to indicate the relationship that exists between the class of amplifier, bias conditions, and amplitude of input signal.

In the class-A amplifier there is an output current for the complete cycle of the input signal. To achieve this, it is biased in the middle of the operating region so that the positive and negative excursions of the input signal will still be in the usable region of the curves, as shown in Fig. 4-2A. To produce a class-B amplifier, the quiescent (Q) point is selected to be at the end of the operating region, as shown in Fig. 4-2B. For positive excursions of the input signal, there is an output current. For negative excursions, there is no base current and thus there is no output current. The class-C amplifier is biased farther away from the operating area than the class-B, as shown in Fig. 4-2C. This allows even less of the input signal to cause an output current.

A more detailed discussion of the three classes of amplifiers is given in the next few sections. Some typical circuits of the class-A, class-B, and class-C amplifiers are described. The advantages and disadvantages of the three different classes are also discussed.

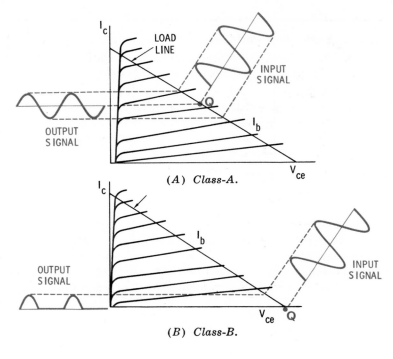

(A) Class-A.

(B) Class-B.

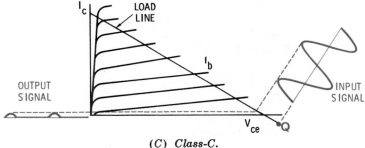

(C) Class-C.

Fig. 4-2. Transistor bias and classes of amplifiers.

Q4-3. The class-_____ amplifier is biased so that less than half a cycle of input signal causes an output current.

Q4-4. From Fig. 4-2 it can be seen that if no signal is applied, the class-_____ amplifier is the only one for which direct current (not signal current) appears in the collector circuit.

CLASS-A AMPLIFIERS

The most practical way to start a description of amplification is with the class-A common-emitter amplifier. The common emitter is the most versatile and widely used configuration, just as the common cathode is the most widely used vacuum-tube configuration. The class-A amplifier is

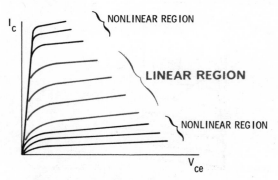

Fig. 4-3. Linearity of output curves.

used where it is desired to amplify a signal without distorting it. By referring to Fig. 4-3 you can see that the section of the load line which would best fulfill this requirement is located in the so-called linear region. It is in this region that equal changes in base current produce equal changes in collector current and voltage. Closer to the cutoff and saturation region the base current lines are not equally spaced and the output will therefore not be a true replica of the input.

98

From what has just been discussed, it can be seen that the choice of a suitable operating point for class-A operation is a function of the amplitude of the signal to be amplified, the requirement being that the largest signal expected should not drive the transistor collector current or voltage

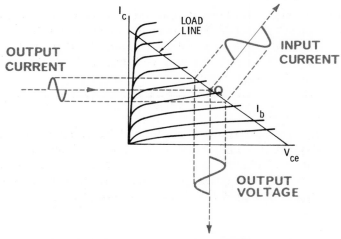

Fig. 4-4. Choice of Q point.

to the regions of nonlinearity. Fig. 4-4 shows a suitable Q point for the size input signal shown. Certain types of transistors are made to be used specifically as amplifiers and will have a large linear region available.

Once a Q point has been selected on the curves, the circuit has to be designed to provide the proper bias to attain the desired Q point. The next section describes biasing techniques for the class-A amplifier.

Q4-5. In the linear region of the output curves, the base current lines (are, are not) equally spaced.

Q4-6. Referring to Fig. 4-4, why is the location of the Q point considered a good one for class-A operation?

Biasing Techniques

Biasing-circuits are used to achieve the desired operating point. Essentially then, biasing involves the selection of a circuit that will provide a desired base current. The desired base current, in turn, has been selected by the choice of operating point. Fig. 4-5 will help to make this clear.

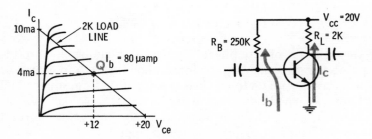

Fig. 4-5. Simple bias arrangement.

Simple Arrangement—Assume that for the type transistor selected, the manufacturer's output curves are as shown in the illustration. The collector load resistor has been selected to be 2000 ohms. The collector supply (V_{cc}) is 20 volts. The Q point has been selected so that $V_{ce} = 12$ volts, and $I_c = 4$ ma. From the curves, it becomes apparent that 80 μamps of base current is required. This can be provided by connecting a resistor (R_B) from the power supply to the base. Neglecting the small voltage drop of the base-to-emitter junction, the correct value of R_B can be calculated:

$$R_B = \frac{V_{cc}}{I_B} = \frac{20 \text{ volts}}{80 \ \mu\text{amp}} = 250{,}000 \text{ ohms}$$

The transistor is then said to be biased (or an operating point established) at $V_{ce} = 12$ volts, and $I_c = 4$ ma.

Limitations—The bias arrangement just described illustrates the principle involved and is a working circuit, but it has a couple of severe practical limitations. The first limitation is that transistors of the same type can have different curves, and thus the base current provided will give different operating points. This is shown in Fig. 4-6. $I_B = 80$ μamps for each case, but the operating point is different. The manufacturer's curves are typical and do not represent the exact curves for each transistor of that type. Not only might the curves be different for different samples of the same type, but at temperatures other than normal room temperatures the curves shift so that again the base current of 80 μamps can lead to different operating points.

The second limitation of the simple bias arrangement described is that no provision is made for I_{co}. This is the leakage current across the base to collector junction with the emitter open. As temperature is increased, I_{co} increases and must be taken into account. The next section describes biasing schemes that help minimize these limitations of the simple arrangement of this section.

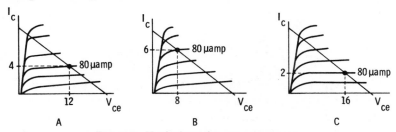

Fig. 4-6. Variations in output curves.

Q4-7. For the common emitter, the operating point is specified by the _____ voltage and _____ current.

Q4-8. From Fig. 4-5 the β of the transistor at the operating point shown is (a) 320 (b) 240 (c) 50 (d) 40.

Improved Arrangements—I_{co} is going to flow between base and collector no matter what steps are taken. The best that can be done is that the circuit be designed so that even though leakage current exists, it does no harm. Fig. 4-7A shows the situation for the simple arrangement of a bias resistor from base to power supply. The I_{co} that flows across the base-collector junction must come through the emitter-base junction; there is no other path to complete its circuit.

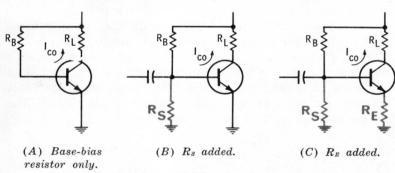

| (A) *Base-bias resistor only.* | (B) *R_s added.* | (C) *R_E added.* |

Fig. 4-7. Improved biasing scheme.

This current through the emitter-base junction produces a current in the collector circuit that is β times the emitter-base current. Thus, the actual collector current includes a βI_{co} component. Since I_{co} varies with temperature, the total collector current varies and the operating point is not very stable. To prevent I_{co} from flowing through the emitter-base junction another path is provided. This is shown in Fig. 4-7B, in which R_s has been added. To further impede the flow of I_{co} through the emitter-base junction, a resistor is added in the emitter lead. This is labeled R_E in Fig. 4-7C. The input resistance to the transistor is $\approx \beta R_E$. The idea then

102

is to make R_s small as compared with βR_E so that I_{co} flows through R_s and not through the emitter-base junction.

To stabilize the operating point against variations in β, an arrangement called self-bias is used. Instead of providing base current by connecting a resistor from the base to the power supply, a resistor is connected from the base to the collector. This is shown as R_F in Fig. 4-8. With this arrangement, the value of the base current is not fixed but rather will depend on the collector voltage. Refer to Fig. 4-6 which shows variations in output curves. If part A represents the average curves for a particular type of transistor, R_F can be calculated:

$$\mathbf{R_F} = \frac{V_{ce}}{I_b} = \frac{12 \text{ volts}}{80 \text{ } \mu\text{amps}} = 150{,}000 \text{ ohms}$$

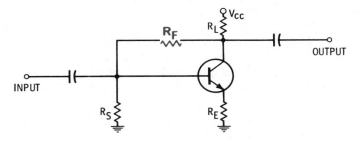

Fig. 4-8. Well-stabilized bias arrangement.

If another transistor of this type happens to have curves like those shown in B, V_{ce} will be smaller, and there is less base current. Since there is less base current, the collector current will be less and V_{ce} will actually increase toward the value shown in A. The operating point is not fixed as it was in the simpler arrangement; instead, it adjusts itself toward the results obtained from using the average curves. Fig. 4-8 shows the complete well-stabilized bias arrangement that takes into account I_{co}, temperature variations, and differences between transistors of the same type.

Q4-9. Is it true that biasing can eliminate I_{co}? Explain.

Q4-10. Self-bias is achieved in the common emitter by connecting a resistor between the _____ and the _____.

Graphic Amplification Analysis

After establishing an operating point by means of biasing circuits, the signal to be amplified can be applied to the circuit. To show graphically what happens, the common-emitter output characteristics are illustrated in Fig. 4-9. The values shown are all assumed values for illustrative purposes. The biasing circuit has established a quiescent point at V_{ce} of 10 volts, and an I_c of 2 ma. Note that a base current of 30 μamps was required to establish this point.

Assume an input signal current of 20 μamps as shown in Fig. 4-9. Since the quiescent base current is 30 μamps, when the signal is applied the base current will vary in one cycle from 30 μamps to 40 μamps, back to 30 μamps, down to 20 μamps and then back to 30 μamps. This change in base current takes place along the load line as shown. As this

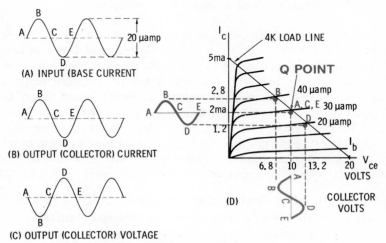

(A) INPUT (BASE CURRENT)

(B) OUTPUT (COLLECTOR) CURRENT

(C) OUTPUT (COLLECTOR) VOLTAGE

(D)

Fig. 4-9. Graphical analysis.

104

change takes place, note what happens along the collector-current axis and the collector-voltage axis. The illustration shows that both the collector current and voltage go through a similar change.

Some important ideas concerning class-A amplification can be derived from Fig. 4-9. If the operating point is selected too near the ends of the load line, clipping will occur in both the collector current and voltage waveshapes. This term is used to describe a signal that has either its top or bottom flattened out, as shown in Fig. 4-10. The current gain can be calculated from Fig. 4-9. I_B is 20 μamps, and I_c can be read off the curves as 1.6 ma. Thus the gain is

$$\text{Current gain} = \frac{I_c}{I_b} = \frac{1.6\text{ ma}}{20\text{ }\mu\text{amp}} = 80$$

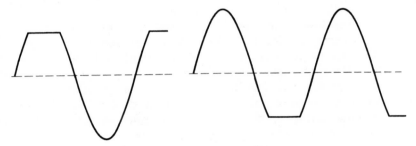

Fig. 4-10. Clipped signals.

The voltage gain can also be calculated. Assume an input resistance of 1000 ohms. With an input current of 20 μamps, the input voltage is 20 mv. The output voltage is read off the curves as 6.4 volts. The voltage gain is:

$$\text{Voltage gain} = \frac{\text{Output volts}}{\text{Input volts}} = \frac{6.4\text{ volts}}{20\text{ mv}} = 320$$

Q4-11. The output voltage of a common-emitter stage (is in phase, is 180 degrees out of phase) with the input voltage.

Q4-12. In the illustration shown in Fig. 4-9, the amount of collector current with no signal applied is _____.

General Comments–Class-A

Of basic importance in the class-A amplifier is the steady value of collector current that exists with the power supply connected, but prior to the introduction of the signal to be amplified. The purpose of the bias circuit is to make this current as stable as possible. One of the best biasing arrangements was discussed in a previous section and is repeated in Fig. 4-11. Capacitor C_3 is included across R_E to provide a low-impedance path for the signal current around R_E. This prevents the development of a voltage across R_E which would tend to counteract the input signal and reduce the gain of the amplifier.

As is usually the case in electronics, to achieve a desired result means compromising in an area that is considered of secondary importance. In the case under discussion, the best bias arrangement leads to a gain less than what can be attained by the simpler arrangement first introduced. This

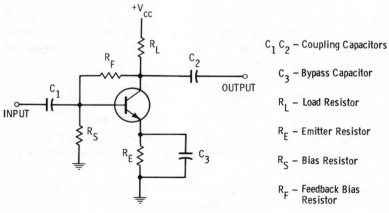

C_1 C_2 – Coupling Capacitors

C_3 – Bypass Capacitor

R_L – Load Resistor

R_E – Emitter Resistor

R_S – Bias Resistor

R_F – Feedback Bias Resistor

Fig. 4-11 Class-A amplifier.

reduction in gain comes about because of the negative feedback caused by R_F, and the fact that R_s will divert to ground some of the signal current that could otherwise be used as base current.

The reduction in gain is well worth it to achieve the primary result. The class-A amplifier is used to reproduce and amplify faithfullly the input signal. Usually the signal is of a low-level amplitude such as might be expected in a radio receiver. After suitable amplification, the signal is ready for power amplification, such as might be used for driving a speaker. For the input signal to be reproduced and amplified faithfully, it is important that the class-A amplifier be operated in the linear region of its output curves. The usual arrangement is a compromise in that some gain is sacrificed to attain good operating-point stability. The loss in gain can be compensated for by adding another stage of amplification.

Where power output and efficiency are of prime importance, class-B amplifiers are used. This is the subject of the next section.

Q4-13. For the output characteristic curves and transistor circuit shown, determine the value of biasing resistor R_F. The Q point has been selected to be on the $I_b = 60$ μamp curve.

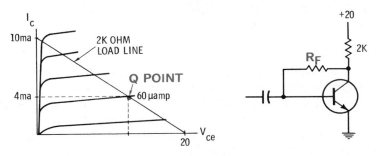

Q4-14. For an input signal of 150 μamps peak-to-peak, has the Q point in Q4-13 been wisely chosen for linear, distortion-free amplification? Why?

CLASS-B AMPLIFIERS

In the class-A amplifiers discussed in the previous section, the excursion of the operating point was limited to the linear region of operation. This was done to prevent distortion that would occur if the signal entered the nonlinear region of the curves. Class-A amplification does suffer from two disadvantages. One of them was pointed out in the previous section. This was the loss in gain that was sacrificed to attain good operating-point stability. More stages of amplification can be added to make up for the loss, so this is not a serious disadvantage.

Power Efficiency

A second disadvantage of the class-A amplifier is the low power efficiency. In general, the efficiency can be considered as the amount of signal power applied to the load, with respect to the power supplied. Recall that the function of the transistor is to convert the direct current from the power supply to useful signal power. Fig. 4-12A shows that even with no signal, the class-A amplifier is drawing collector current and dissipating power. The class-B amplifier does not draw collector current with no signal, as pointed out in

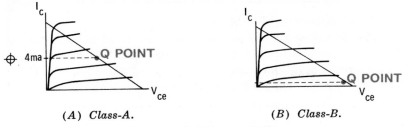

(A) Class-A.   *(B) Class-B.*

Fig. 4-12. Quiescent points.

Fig. 4-12B. When the class-B amplifier does draw current, it is for useful signal power.

Distortion

If in a circuit used as a class-A amplifier, the bias was changed to produce a class-B amplifier, a condition as shown in Fig. 4-13 would result. The output signal is a poor reproduction of the input signal. If the signal being amplified was speech or music, much distortion would result. To minimize this problem when class-B amplifiers are used for reasons of high power output and power efficiency, a different scheme is used. The next section shows how circuits can be arranged to take advantage of the good qualities of the class-B amplifier and eliminate the distortion.

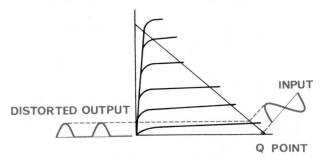

Fig. 4-13. Distortion.

Q4-15. When no signal is applied, the class-_____ amplifier dissipates power, while the class-_____ does not.

Q4-16. One of the main advantages of a class-B amplifier is that it has good _____ efficiency.

Class-B Circuits

From Fig. 4-13 it was seen that there is an output current only for the positive swings of the input current. If an arrangement could be made so that there is an output current for both positive and negative swings, then the distortion referred to in connection with the illustration would be eliminated. Two types of arrangements that do just this will be discussed.

Complementary-Symmetry Circuit—An NPN transistor conducts when the base is made more positive than the emitter; a PNP transistor conducts when the base is made more negative than the emitter. Each of these situations is shown in the illustration for a common-collector (or emitter-follower) configuration. In Fig. 4-14A only the positive excursion of the input signal is passed to the load resistor, R_L. In Fig. 4-14B, only the negative swing is passed to R_L.

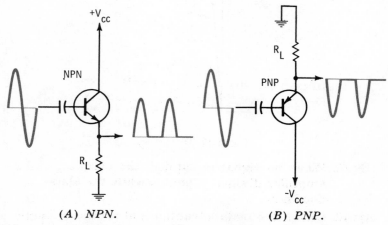

(A) NPN. (B) PNP.

Fig. 4-14. Signal flow in NPN and PNP emitter followers.

110

Both stages have zero bias and can then be considered as class-B amplifiers. Note that they are emitter-followers and thus will give only current (or power) gain, not voltage gain. Power gain is what is needed in an output stage to drive low-impedance devices such as speakers. The two circuits combined with one input and one output are shown in Fig. 4-15. This is called a complementary-symmetry circuit. The action is the same as it is for the NPN and PNP operating separately. For the positive excursion of the input signal, the NPN transistor conducts and the PNP is off. For the negative swing of the signal, the opposite is true. Note that with no signal applied, neither transistor is conducting.

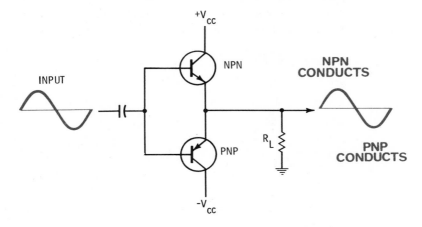

Fig. 4-15. Complementary-symmetry common-collector circuit.

Q4-17. The complementary-symmetry circuit shown above is really a pair of transistors in the grounded-_____ configuration.

Q4-18. Since zero base-current bias is supplied to the circuit, both the NPN and PNP transistors are operated class-_____.

Your Answers Should Be:

A4-17. The complementary-symmetry circuit is really a pair of transistors in the grounded-**collector** configuration.

A4-18. Since zero base-current bias is supplied to the circuit, both the NPN and PNP transistors are operated class-B.

Push-Pull Circuit—Another common circuit used for class-B amplification is the so-called push-pull amplifier shown in Fig. 4-16. Both transistors in the example are of the NPN type, but they could just as well be PNP type if the power-supply polarity was reversed. For this type of

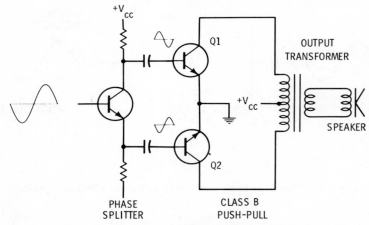

Fig. 4-16. Standard push-pull class-B amplifier.

circuit, two signals that are 180 degrees out of phase are required. One way to obtain these signals is by the use of a phase splitter. This circuit provides one signal from the collector, and from the emitter, a signal 180 degrees out of phase with the other signal. As the signal at the collector swings positive, transistor Q1 conducts. At the same time, transistor Q2 is cut off because the signal at the emitter is swinging negative at this time. During the next half-cycle, transistor Q2 is on and Q1 is off. In this way there is always a signal current through the output transformer, even though each transistor conducts for only half the cycle. This type of class-B push-pull amplifier is used mainly in applications requiring high-power output and high efficiency, such as driving a speaker.

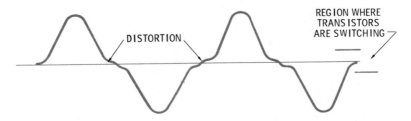

Fig. 4-17. Crossover distortion.

One characteristic of class-B push-pull amplifiers that should be mentioned is crossover distortion, which is shown in Fig. 4-17. Crossover distortion is the result of the non-linearity of the output curves near the cutoff region. The "on" transistor approaches cutoff from the linear region as it turns off, and the "off" transistor leaves the cutoff region as it turns on. This is why the distortion occurs in the region where the transistors are switching. One way of minimizing this distortion is to supply a small forward bias to each transistor. Strictly speaking, the circuit is then no longer a class-B amplifier, but rather it is between a class-B and class-A and is sometimes referred to as a class-AB amplifier.

The last class of amplifiers to be considered is the class-C which will be covered in the next section.

Q4-19. Each transistor in the push-pull arrangement conducts for a (an) _____-cycle of the input signal.

Q4-20. Crossover distortion, a characteristic of class-B amplifiers, is due to the transistors operating near the (saturation, cutoff) region.

Your Answers Should Be:

A4-19. Each transistor in the push-pull arrangement conducts for a **half**-cycle of the input signal.

A4-20. Crossover distortion, a characteristic of class-B amplifiers, is due to the transistors operating in the **cutoff** region.

CLASS-C AMPLIFIERS

When power output and efficiency are of prime consideration, a class-B amplifier is used instead of a class-A amplifier. When the bias is designed to be beyond the cutoff value used in class-B operation, further increases in plate efficiency and power output are achieved. When so arranged, the circuit is called a class-C amplifier.

Limitations

Because it is biased beyond cutoff, the class-C amplifier is useful only for certain applications. Fig. 4-18 shows why

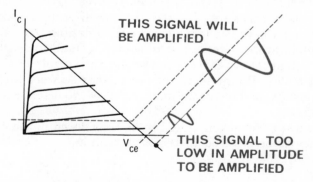

Fig. 4-18. Certain amplitude signal required.

this class of amplifier has limitations. For low-level signals, the amplitude of the signal might not be large enough to turn the transistor on. (There is a certain amplitude signal that is required to turn the transistor on, depending on how far beyond cutoff the transistor is biased.) The class-C amplifier is therefore not suited for amplifying a signal of

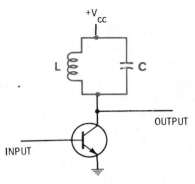

Fig. 4-19. Tuned circuit.

varying amplitude, and it is ordinarily used for amplifying a signal of fixed amplitude.

Tuned Circuits

The class-C amplifier cannot be used in an RC amplifier or in push-pull configuration because large signal distortion would result. In general, the push-pull connection is biased class-B (or class-AB) and is used for signals in the low or audio-frequency range. The class-C amplifier is generally used with an arrangement called a tuned circuit. This connection is applicable mainly at radio frequencies. Fig. 4-19 shows a simple tuned circuit. The load resistor is replaced by a capacitor and inductor that are resonant at the frequency of the signal being amplified. The tuned circuit can also be used with class-A and class-B amplifiers, so it is covered in a later section where other interstage coupling circuits are discussed.

The next section discusses how a transistor circuit can be biased beyond cutoff.

Q4-21. Why can't a class-C amplifier be used to amplify low-level signals?

Q4-22. In general, class-C amplifiers use an arrangement called a _____ _____.

Q4-23. The most simple tuned circuit consists of a (an) _____ and _____, whose values are selected to produce resonance at the frequency of interest.

115

Class-C Bias

In order to have a common-emitter NPN stage biased beyond cutoff (class-C condition), the voltage at the base must be more negative than that at the emitter. One way to achieve this is by a resistor divider scheme as shown in Fig. 4-20A. A second source of voltage is required and this voltage is labeled $-V_{cc}$. The resistors R_B and R_S are selected to make V_B negative. Fig. 4-20B shows an example in which V_B is biased to -1 volt. The signal to be amplified is superimposed on the bias voltage. The transistor stays off until V_B reaches $+1$ volt, and then it conducts while the signal

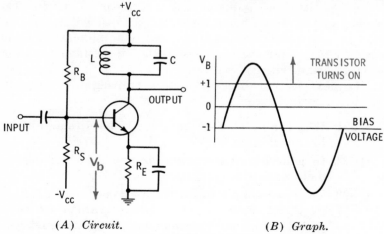

(A) *Circuit.*   (B) *Graph.*

Fig. 4-20. Class-C bias.

remains above +1 volt. Notice in Fig. 4-20B that the transistor is on for considerably less than a half-cycle of the input signal. This fulfills the requirement for calling this a class-C amplifier. How these "spurts" of input signal can lead to a smooth sine-wave output signal is covered in the section on tuned circuits.

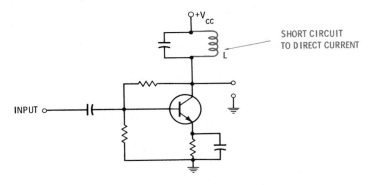

Fig. 4-21. Tuned-circuit biasing.

Note in Fig. 4-20A that resistor R_B is connected from base to +V_{cc}. It has been explained that in class-A circuits better operating-point stability could be achieved by connecting this resistor from the base to the collector. However, the inductor in a tuned circuit can be considered as a short circuit to direct current. For this reason, connecting the resistor to +V_{cc} or the collector produces the same effect on the d-c operating-point stability. However, connecting the resistor to the collector produces negative feedback to the input signal and will lower the gain of the stage without the benefit of operating-point stability. For this reason the biasing resistor is connected to +V_{cc} as shown in Fig. 4-2. Just as for a class-A amplifier, an emitter resistor, R_E, and a bypass capacitor are used to aid in d-c temperature stability.

Q4-24. In the class-C grounded-emitter amplifier, the base-to-emitter junction is (forward, reverse) biased by the biasing circuit.

Q4-25. The type of biasing arrangement used in an RC circuit is not possible in a tuned circuit because the _____ is a short circuit to direct current.

GENERAL COMMENTS

The last few sections have described the three main classes of amplifiers. This section will summarize the situation and point out some advantages and disadvantages.

Class-A

In the class-A amplifier, the operating point is selected in the linear region of the transistor characteristics. The output waveshape closely resembles the input signal. This type of amplifier is used where low-level signals are to be amplified and a minimum of distortion is required. It is usually not used to deliver a relatively large amount of power nor is it very efficient.

Class-B

The operating point of the class-B amplifier is located at the cutoff point of the output characteristic curves. The primary objectives of such an arrangement is to minimize the average collector current and thus conserve power and increase efficiency. However, these advantages are attained at the cost of faithful reproduction. The usual class-B amplifier is arranged in a push-pull scheme. Quite often, the stage that drives a speaker is a class-B push-pull stage. Whereas the class-A amplifier can be used over a wide range of frequencies, the class-B amplifier is applicable throughout the low- or audio-frequency range.

Class-C

The class-C amplifier is biased beyond the cutoff value used in class-B operation. For this reason, the class-C amplifier requires a certain minimum amplitude input signal. This type of amplifier is not particularly well suited for amplifying an input signal of varying amplitude, and is ordinarily used for amplifying fixed-amplitude signals. Usually, the class-C amplifier has a tuned-circuit load and is used at radio frequencies.

Q4-26. Indicate whether the statements below are true or false for the type of amplifier they are listed under:

1. Class-A amplifier
   (a) Least efficient of the three types of amplifiers. _____
   (b) Efficiency sacrificed in order to provide faithful, distortion-free amplification. _____
   (c) One of main applications is to drive speakers, such as in a radio. _____
   (d) Biased in linear region of output characteristic curves. _____

2. Class-B amplifier
   (a) When no signal is applied, draws more collector current than a class-A amplifier: _____
   (b) Produces more distortion than the class-A amplifier. _____
   (c) Used mainly as an output power stage. _____
   (d) In push-pull arrangement, requires two transistors. _____

3. Class-C amplifier
   (a) Used mainly for amplifying low-level signals. _____
   (b) When used as tuned amplifier, more efficient than a class-A amplifier. _____
   (c) Requires a certain minimum-amplitude input signal. _____
   (d) Biased in saturation region of output characteristic curves. _____

COUPLING NETWORKS

RC Network

The RC amplifier is a basic multipurpose amplifier. It is so called because there is a resistor for the collector load and a capacitor to couple the signal to the next stage. Fig. 4-22A shows a two-stage RC coupled amplifier. When the output of one amplifier is connected to the input of another, the two amplifiers are connected in cascade. The reason for using cascaded circuits is to increase overall gain.

The RC amplifier is widely used because it is simple to design, and uses a minimum of components. It can be used to amplify signals in a wide range of often-used frequencies, as shown in Fig. 4-22B, where a gain-versus-frequency plot is illustrated. The numbers in the illustration are intended to show a general frequency region and not specific cutoff frequencies.

RC Amplifier Limitations—The RC amplifier has limitations that give rise to other types of coupling networks. Fig.

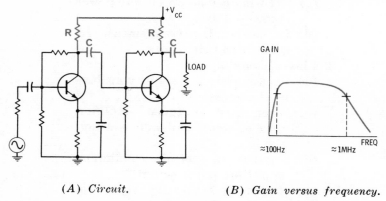

(A) *Circuit.*   (B) *Gain versus frequency.*

Fig. 4-22. RC coupling network.

120

4-23 details the nature of the limitations. The first limitation is the coupling capacitor itself. A capacitor will not pass a d-c signal. Therefore, if circuit specifications require passing a d-c signal, or a very low-frequency signal, the capacitor will block it. This limitation is overcome by using a so-called direct-coupled amplifier, in which the capacitor is left out. A second limitation of the RC amplifier is stray capacitance which limits the gain at high frequencies. Stray capacitances cannot be completely eliminated (although they can be minimized); they result from the physical position of the component near ground points. The impedance of a capacitor decreases as frequency is increased, and a larger portion of the signal will be shunted to ground instead of being passed on to the next stage. To extend the range of frequencies over which the RC amplifier is useful, another component is added. This component is an inductor, and the new circuit is called a shunt-peaked amplifier.

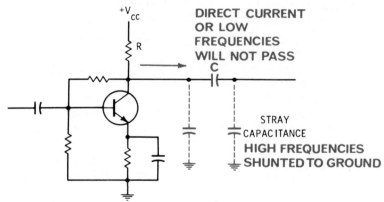

Fig. 4-23. High- and low-frequency limitations.

Q4-27. When the output of one amplifier feeds the input of a second amplifier, the two amplifiers are in
_____.

Q4-28. A direct-current (or low-frequency) signal will not be passed by an RC circuit because of the
_____.

Q4-29. Stray _____ between the components and ground limits the high-frequency amplification capabilities of the RC amplifier.

D-C Amplifier

A typical two stage direct-coupled amplifier is shown in Fig. 4-24A. The main difference between this circuit and the RC amplifier is that the coupling capacitor is not included in the direct-coupled amplifier. The purpose of the coupling capacitor in the RC amplifier was to prevent the d-c biasing currents from being affected by the other stage. Since the capacitor is now being left out to fulfill the circuit requirement of amplifying d-c signals, the biasing circuits have to be carefully designed to take into account the interaction of the two circuits. One of the main drawbacks to this type of coupling is that any change or drift in bias is coupled to the next stage. More complicated circuits can be utilized to minimize this drift problem. The plot of gain versus frequency for this circuit is shown in Fig. 4-24B. Note the difference at direct current (0 frequency) between this plot and the one for the RC amplifier.

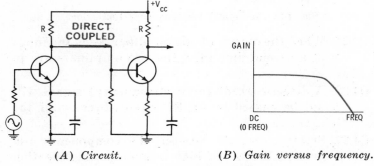

(A) Circuit.   (B) Gain versus frequency.

Fig. 4-24. Direct-coupled amplifier.

Shunt-Peaked Amplifier

The amplifier discussed in this section is really a single type in a large classification called wideband or video amplifiers. The shunt-peaked amplifier was selected because it illustrates the general way of dealing with the stray capacitance. It is called a video amplifier because it was developed to amplify the video signal in television.

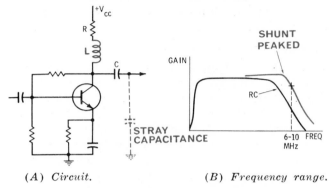

(A) *Circuit.*   (B) *Frequency range.*

Fig. 4-25. Shunt-peaked amplifier.

The actual technique is to start with an RC circuit and use an inductor to "tune out" the stray capacitance. The inductor is placed in series with the resistor in the collector circuit as shown in Fig. 4-25A. Its value is selected to resonate with the stray capacitance at approximately the frequency at which the stray capacitance starts shunting the signal to ground. The inductor is called the peaking inductor. Fig. 4-25B shows the wider frequency range of the shunt-peaked amplifier as compared to the conventional RC amplifier. Usually, video amplifiers can amplify signals up to the 6-to-10 megahertz region.

Q4-30. **A direct-coupled amplifier is similar in configuration to an RC amplifier, except that the _____ has been removed.**

Q4-31. **A coil, called the _____ coil, is added in series with the _____ in the collector circuit of an RC amplifier to form a type of video amplifier called the _____-peaked amplifier.**

Transformer-Coupled Amplifier

The transformer-coupled amplifier has already been introduced in the section covering the standard class-B push-pull amplifier. Transformers can be used in class-A amplifiers also, as seen in Fig. 4-26A. The use of most transformer-coupled amplifiers is limited to the audio-frequency range, as shown in Fig. 4-26B. Thus the frequency response is not as good as that of the RC amplifier. In addition, transformers are big in size and more expensive than resistors and capacitors. However, transformer-coupled amplifiers have high power efficiency and can deliver large amounts of power. Thus, they are generally confined to applications where power efficiency and power output are important.

Tuned-Circuit Amplifier

Tuned-circuit amplifiers were mentioned in the section on class-C amplifiers. However, they can be operated as any

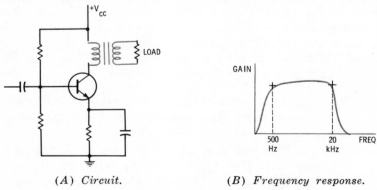

(A) *Circuit.*　　　　　(B) *Frequency response.*

Fig. 4-26. Transformer-coupled amplifier.

one of the three classes. Fig. 4-27A shows a simple parallel resonant-tuned circuit. The components that make up the tuned circuit, the L and C, are placed in parallel in the collector circuit. Tuned amplifiers are used to amplify only a selected bandwidth of frequencies, as shown in Fig. 4-27B.

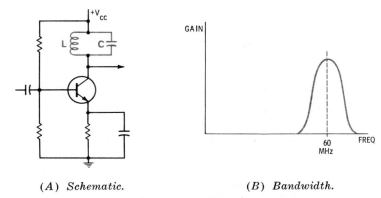

(A) Schematic.   (B) Bandwidth.

Fig. 4-27. Tuned circuit.

Usually, the band of frequencies to be amplified is above 10 megahertz. Fig. 4-27 shows an example in which the center of the band of frequencies being amplified is at 60 megahertz. The band of frequencies to be amplified is governed by the important relationship:

$$f_r = \frac{1}{2\pi\sqrt{LC}}$$

where,
f_r is the resonant frequency in hertz,
L is the inductance in henrys,
C is the capacitance in farads.

This type of circuit is used extensively in radio, radar, and television, where the frequencies involved require tuned-circuit amplifiers.

Q4-32. The (transformer-coupled, tuned-circuit) amplifier is usually used at audio frequencies.

Q4-33. In the tuned circuit, a (an) _____ and _____ replace the resistor in the collector circuit of an RC amplifier.

125

SUMMARY QUESTIONS

1. This chapter described the three main classes of amplifiers. The class-A amplifier is biased in the linear region of its characteristic curves and there is an output current for the complete cycle. The class-B amplifier is biased at cutoff and there is an output current for only half of a cycle (180 degrees). The class-C amplifier is biased beyond cutoff with the result that there is an output current for less than half of a cycle. The class-A amplifier is usually used for low-level distortion-free amplification. The class-B amplifier is used for output stages, since it provides good power efficiency and can deliver relatively large amounts of power. One of the most common applications is in the audio frequency range where it is used to drive speakers. The class-C amplifier finds most of its applications in the high-frequency region where tuned circuits are used. In most of the descriptions the NPN transistor was used but the PNP could have been used just as well. The common-emitter configuration was used because it is the most versatile and the most widely employed.

   a. Because it is biased to avoid the cutoff and saturation regions, the class-_____ amplifier is used for low-level, distortion-free amplification.

   b. One of the most popular class-_____ amplifiers is the push-pull type.

2. The biasing of a class-A amplifier is important because it is essential to keep the operating point in the linear region. It was shown in this chapter that the simple biasing method of connecting a resistor from the power supply to the base (common-emitter configuration) is a

poor way to bias a transistor. It would cause the amplifier to be sensitive to both transistor replacement and change in temperature. A more practical arrangement consists of a resistor from collector to the base and a resistor in the emitter lead which is usually by-passed with a capacitor. This type of biasing sacrifices gain for good operating point stability.

a. The operating point of the common-emitter configuration is specified by the ＿＿＿＿＿ to emitter voltage and ＿＿＿＿＿ current.

3. The basic RC amplifier has limitations that lead to the use of other types of coupling networks. The coupling capacitor limits the low-frequency response, and stray capacitance limits the high-frequency response. The other types of coupling networks mentioned in this chapter are the direct-coupled, transformer-coupled, shunt-peaked, and tuned circuits.

a. The illustration shows typical responses of the five types of coupling networks described in this chapter. Label each curve with one of the types listed.

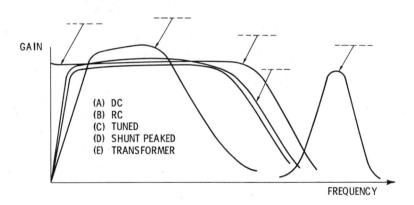

GAIN

(A) DC
(B) RC
(C) TUNED
(D) SHUNT PEAKED
(E) TRANSFORMER

FREQUENCY

SUMMARY ANSWERS

1a. Because it is biased to avoid the cutoff and saturation regions, the class-**A** amplifier is used for low-level, distortion-free amplification.

1b. One of the most popular class-**B** amplifiers is the push-pull type.

2a. The operating point of the common-emitter configuration is specified by the **collector** to emitter voltage and **collector** current.

3a.

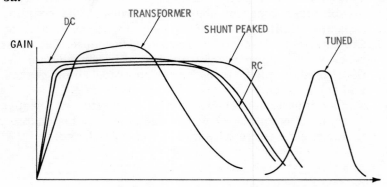

5

Transistor
Oscillator Circuits

Oscillators are electronic circuits that convert direct-current power into alternating-current power. Amplifiers accomplish the same thing but with one important difference. In amplifiers, d-c power from a power supply is converted into a-c power under the control of an external signal applied to the input. Ordinarily, oscillators make this conversion without the aid of an externally supplied input signal.

This chapter begins with a section that describes the important role that oscillators play in all types of electronic systems. All radar, radio and television receivers, and transmitters contain oscillator circuits. It is a rare electronic system that does not contain an oscillator of some sort.

As is the case with amplifiers, there are many different ways to classify oscillators. One of the most convenient methods, and the one adopted in this book, depends on the shape of the output signal. If the output signal is sinusoidal, the circuit is a sinusoidal oscillator; if the output signal is nonsinusoidal, such as a square wave, the circuit is called a relaxation oscillator. The basic principles and essential components of all oscillators are presented before individual circuits are described. Circuits using various networks to produce oscillation are then analyzed.

ESSENTIAL ROLE OF OSCILLATORS

A very important function of oscillators in large electronic systems is to establish a time reference. An oscillator generates a signal with a precise number of cycles or pulses per second. When used as the basic time reference, an oscillator is called a "master clock." This "master clock" enables the entire system to be operated with precision. For instance, a radar does not transmit a pulse of energy in a random fashion, but at a definite rate of so many pulses per second as determined by a "master clock" oscillator in the system.

Large-scale digital computers use oscillators in the role of master clocks, as shown in the illustration. Fig. 5-1 shows master-timing pulses as the output of an oscillator circuit that has only d-c power supplied to it. These timing pulses are used throughout the system to trigger other circuits that perform the required functions in a certain time sequence.

Oscillators are widely used in the communications field when radio-frequency (r-f) signals are transmitted and received. One such application is the use of an oscillator to generate the r-f carrier signal in a transmitter, such as a radio, television, or radar transmitter. The carrier signal is modulated by the information signal (audio in the case of radio) and transmitted. At the receiver, an oscillator is used

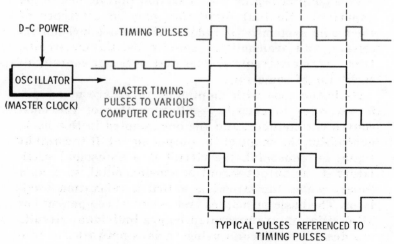

Fig. 5-1. Master clock for digital computer.

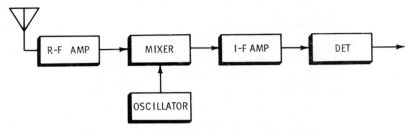

Fig. 5-2. Typical superheterodyne front end.

in another role. The block diagram in Fig. 5-2 shows the "front end" of a typical superheterodyne receiver. The oscillator generates a signal that mixes with or beats with the received r-f signal. The result is a new signal called the intermediate-frequency (i-f) signal. The i-f signal, which retains all the modulating information of the original carrier, is amplified by the i-f amplifier for further processing. The two oscillator applications just mentioned only begin to point out the important part that oscillators play in the field of communications.

Many types of laboratory test equipment use oscillators as the basic timing device or signal source. Two such instruments are sine-wave generators and pulse generators.

Q5-1. An important difference between amplifiers and oscillators is that _____ produce an output under the influence of an input signal, while _____ require only the application of d-c power to produce an output.

BASIC PRINCIPLES

All the oscillators to be studied in this book operate on the same basic principles. This section will explain these principles in a general way, and subsequent sections will apply them to specific circuits.

Amplifier With Feedback

The circuit shown in Fig. 5-3A is a conventional amplifier with an input and output. If the input is removed there is no output. Suppose now that a portion of the output signal

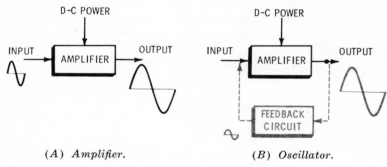

(A) Amplifier. *(B) Oscillator.*

Fig. 5-3. Amplifier with feedback.

is connected back to the input through a feedback circuit, as shown in Fig. 5-3B. Under certain conditions to be described later, this signal being fed back could take the place of the externally applied input signal. The situation now exists in which the externally applied input signal is removed and a portion of the output signal is used in its place. Thus the circuit is producing an a-c output with no externally applied input. This brings up the question of how the circuit starts in the first place, since an output cannot be attained until a portion of the output is fed back to the input. This apparent dilemma will be resolved in a subsequent section.

Negative and Positive Feedback—The term feedback is used to describe the situation in which a percentage of the output signal is fed back to the input. This signal that is fed

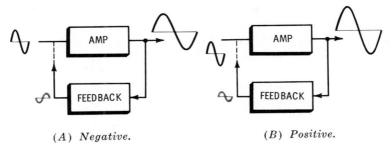

(A) *Negative.*   (B) *Positive.*

Fig. 5-4. Negative and positive feedback.

back is either in phase or 180 degrees out of phase with the input signal. When it is 180 degrees out of phase with the input signal, the result is a smaller amplitude signal entering the amplifier because the signal which is fed back actually subtracts from the original signal. This is called negative feedback, as shown in Fig. 5-4A. If the signal fed back is in phase with the input signal, it adds to this signal and the signal entering the amplifier is larger (and so is the output) than the original signal. This is called positive feedback and is shown in Fig. 5-4B.

There are certain advantages to applying negative feedback to an amplifier. These all have to do with its characteristics as an amplifier. However, to produce an oscillator, positive feedback is required. The signal fed back has the correct phase to make the output signal larger.

Q5-2. In broad terms, an oscillator could be thought of as an amplifier that has _____ _____ applied to it. This removes the requirements for an externally applied _____ signal.

Positive Feedback for Oscillation—The previous section explained the concept of feedback. To produce an oscillator, it was pointed out that some means of applying positive feedback had to be devised. Fig. 5-5 shows the block diagram of a circuit in which the amplifier is shown as a block separate from the feedback circuit. The feedback network is connected to a point toward the output of the amplifier circuit so that after the signal goes through the feedback network, it is applied back into the amplifier with the correct phase

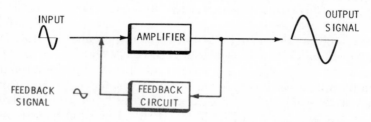

Fig. 5-5. Positive feedback.

to cause the output signal to increase in amplitude. The signal increases till the circuit is saturated and then remains at that amplitude. This is why it is called positive feedback. One can see that if the feedback signal is 180 degrees out of phase with that shown in the illustration it would subtract from the input signal and the output would get smaller. That type of feedback is called negative feedback. The next section explains how the oscillator makes use of positive feedback to sustain oscillation without an externally applied input signal. It should be mentioned that not all oscillator circuits can be conveniently divided into amplifier and feedback blocks as shown in the illustration, although they will operate on the same principle.

134

How the Oscillator Starts

An apparent dilemma was mentioned a few sections before this when it was explained that an oscillator takes a percentage of the output signal and feeds it back to the input, thus taking the place of the externally applied input signal. The question arose as to how an output signal appears in the first place if there is no externally applied input signal.

The answer to the problem is that the oscillator depends on small disturbances in the circuit to produce an output of sufficient amplitude to start the feedback process. The disturbance that is almost always counted on to start the oscillator is the switching surge accompanying the application of the d-c supply. The frequency-selective circuits in the amplifier respond to this disturbance and an output appears. The time buildup of this output signal continues if the gain of the amplifier is sufficiently large to amplify the feedback signal to produce the output signal. An important consideration in the design of an oscillator is to make sure it starts oscillating with the application of the d-c supply.

Note that it does not matter whether the disturbance produces an initial output that is positive or negative in amplitude. The important point is that the signal fed back is the correct phase with respect to the output signal and that the amplifier has sufficient gain to sustain oscillation.

Q5-4. If the feedback signal is 180 degrees out of phase with the input signal to an amplifier, it is said to be _____ feedback.

Q5-5. If the feedback signal is in phase with the input signal to an amplifier, it is said to be _____ feedback.

Q5-6. What usually starts an oscillator?

TYPES OF OSCILLATORS

The oscillators described in this book are divided into two categories. The first type includes the oscillators that produce a sine-wave output or at least nearly a sine wave. The second type is the relaxation oscillator in which the output is a square wave. The oscillators are itemized here and will be discussed in more detail in subsequent sections.

Sinusoidal Oscillators

The three most common types of sinusoidal oscillators will now be discussed. The item that distinguishes one from the other is the frequency-determining element. The types of oscillators are named according to these elements, as shown in Fig. 5-6. They are the LC, RC and crystal-controlled oscillators.

LC Oscillator—As the name implies, this type of oscillator depends on an LC tank circuit to determine its frequency of operation. This type of circuit can be used at audio or radio frequencies and provides reasonably good frequency stability.

RC Oscillator—The usual configuration for this type of oscillator uses three RC sections to determine the frequency of oscillation. These oscillators are used in the audio-frequency range and are particularly useful if a large range of frequencies must be covered.

Crystal-Controlled—The frequency of oscillation of this type of circuit essentially is fixed by the crystal that is used.

It is used when the best frequency stability is required from the middle of the audio range through the r-f range.

Relaxation Oscillator

The type of relaxation oscillator to be studied in this chapter is called an astable multivibrator. It is a symmetrical type of circuit as shown in Fig. 5-6. This type of circuit is really a two stage oscillator in which one transistor is on and the other off until a time is reached when this condition switches, thus producing a square-wave output.

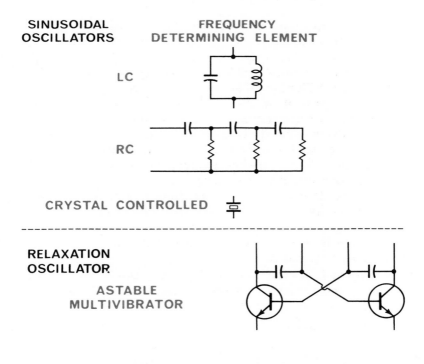

Fig. 5-6. Types of oscillators.

Q5-7. _____ type of oscillators produce the best frequency stability and can be used in the r-f range.

Q5-8. The _____ oscillator produces a square-wave output because the transistors actually act as switches which turn on and off.

LC OSCILLATORS

The elements that characterize the LC oscillator are the inductor and capacitor themselves. They form a resonant or tank circuit that determines the frequency of oscillation.

An elementary resonant circuit is illustrated in Fig. 5-7. A parallel combination of an inductor and capacitor can have power applied to it by closing the switch. When the switch is closed, the capacitor starts to charge and the inductor starts to draw current. This action creates an electrostatic field in the capacitor and an electromagnetic field in the coil. Both of these fields store energy, which is why this circuit is called a tank circuit. The energy passes from one type of field to the other and back again, thus producing a voltage across the tank, as shown in Fig. 5-7. The length of time it takes for the oscillation to die out depends on the resistance in the circuit. The frequency of the oscillations depends on the values of L and C.

Frequency of Oscillation—The LC tuned circuit determines the frequency of oscillation in the LC oscillator.

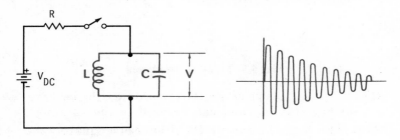

Fig. 5-7. LC tank circuit.

The very important expression relating the frequency with the values of L and C is:

$$f = \frac{1}{2\pi\sqrt{LC}}$$

where,

f is the frequency in hertz,
L is the inductance in henrys,
C is the capacitance in farads.

The following example will show the use of this formula. Find the frequency of oscillation if the inductance is 1 millihenry and the capacitance is 0.1 microfarad:

$$f = \frac{1}{2\pi\sqrt{LC}}$$

$$= \frac{1}{2\pi\sqrt{1 \times 10^{-3} \times .1 \times 10^{-6}}}$$

$$= \frac{1}{2\pi\sqrt{1 \times 10^{-10}}}$$

$$= \frac{1}{6.28 \times 10^{-5}}$$

$$f = 16,000 \text{ hertz}$$

Note that in the discussion so far, the oscillations die out. This is where the amplifier part of the oscillator comes into play. Part of the oscillation will be fed back into the amplifier and energy will be supplied to the tank circuit at just the right time to sustain oscillation.

Q5-9. The approximate value of the inductance that will resonate with a 1-microfarad capacitor to produce a frequency of 20,000 hertz is _____.

Feedback Signals—The previous section described the resonant or tank circuit and how an alternating signal is generated by the passage of energy back and forth between the capacitor and inductor. The signal to be fed back to

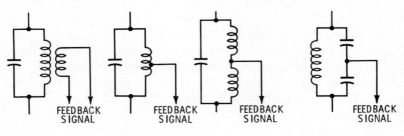

(A) *Inductive tap.*   (B) *Capacitive tap.*

Fig. 5-8. Feedback signals

sustain oscillation is derived from this circuit by either of two means. The first method is to take some of the energy from the inductor. This can be done by any of the three circuits shown in Fig. 5-8A. When an oscillator uses a tapped coil for the feedback signal it is called a Hartley oscillator. A second means of deriving the feedback signal is to use two capacitors in the tank circuit and tap off in between them. This is shown in Fig. 5-8B. A circuit employing this scheme is called a Colpitts oscillator.

Circuit Example

An LC oscillator is shown in Fig. 5-9. The circuit is a Colpitts oscillator because the feedback signal is taken from the junction of the two capacitors in the tank circuit. Resistors R1, R2, and R3 are bias resistors. The tank circuit consists of L1 in resonance with the series combination of C1 and C2. The feedback signal is applied by the connection from the junction of C1 and C2 to the emitter of the transistor. A Hartley oscillator would have almost the same configuration with the significant difference being that the feedback signal would be derived from the tank-circuit inductor. A PNP transistor could have been shown just as well provided the polarity of V_{cc} were reversed.

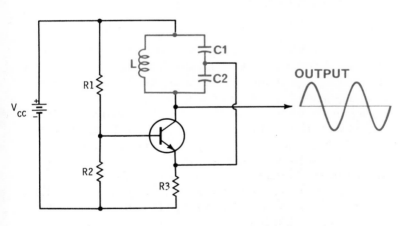

Fig. 5-9. Colpitts oscillator.

Q5-10. The _____ oscillator obtains the feedback signal from the tank circuit inductor.

Q5-11. In the illustration of Fig. 5-9, the frequency of oscillation is determined by (a) L1 resonating with C1, (b) L1 resonating with the parallel combination of C1 and C2, (c) L1 resonating with the series combination of C1 and C2, or (d) time constant associated with L1 and R3.

141

CRYSTAL-CONTROLLED OSCILLATORS

For best frequency stability, a crystal-controlled oscillator is used. This circuit will hold its frequency of oscillation better than other circuits under conditions of varying load, supply voltages, temperature, etc. Since this oscillator depends on a crystal for its operation, the pertinent characteristics of a crystal will be described.

Crystals

Certain crystalline substances exhibit an interesting phenomenon called the piezoelectric effect. This effect can be described in the following way: If the crystalline substance is connected to an alternating signal, the crystal actually changes physical shape, and these changes cause mechanical vibrations. These mechanical vibrations, in turn, develop a voltage across the crystal. The most suitable crystalline substance for use in oscillator circuits is quartz.

Crystal Characteristics—The electrical equivalent circuit of the crystal is shown in Fig. 5-10. The equivalent circuit consists of a resistance R, an inductance L, and a capacitance C_s. The capacitance labeled C_p is the stray capacitance across the terminals of the crystal. The crystal is drawn on schematics with the symbol shown in Fig. 5-11.

The mechanical resonant frequency of a crystal is determined by its dimensions. The types of crystals used in

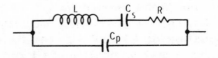

Fig. 5-10. Crystal equivalent circuit.

oscillator circuits must be cut and ground to extremely accurate dimensions. Suppose that a signal which has the same frequency as the resonant frequency of the crystal is applied to the crystal. Only a small voltage need be applied to keep the crystal vibrating. In turn, the crystal will generate a large signal at its resonant frequency. If the frequency of the applied signal is slightly higher or lower

Fig. 5-11. Crystal symbol.

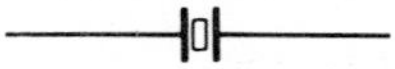

than the crystal resonant frequency, the amount of mechanical vibrations is almost zero. The crystal stops vibrating and no voltage is produced. Thus it can be seen that the frequency of a crystal-controlled oscillator has to be the same as the crystal, or else it probably will not oscillate at all.

In most applications, the series circuit of L and C_s is used to establish the resonant frequency. However, it is possible to use the parallel combination of L and C_p as the resonant circuit. Resonance would occur at a slightly higher frequency than with the series mode of operation. The type of circuit in which the crystal is being used will determine which combination is to be used.

Q5-12. If a mechanical force is applied to a crystal, a voltage is generated, and vice versa. This is known as the _____ effect.

Q5-13. The crystal may be used as a series circuit consisting of L and _____, or a parallel circuit of L and _____.

Circuit Examples

The circuit shown in Fig. 5-12 is a relatively simple crystal-controlled oscillator. The crystal unit is placed in series with the feedback path from the tuned circuit to the emitter of the transistor. Note that a crystal is designated on a schematic with the letter Y. Resistors R1, R2, and R3

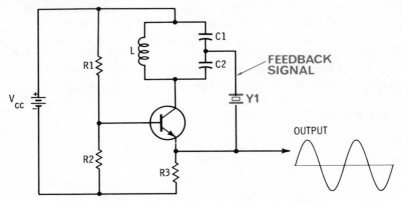

Fig. 5-12. Series crystal-controlled oscillator.

provide the proper biasing conditions for the circuit. The resonant circuit consists of L in parallel with the series combination of C1 and C2. When the resonant frequency of the tank circuit equals the series-resonant frequency of the crystal, a large enough signal is fed back to the emitter to sustain oscillation. At higher or lower frequencies than resonance, the crystal is a high-impedance device and attenuates the feedback signal so that oscillations stop.

The crystal-controlled oscillator shown in Fig. 5-13 uses the crystal in the parallel mode. This means that it is

144

operated at a frequency at which the crystal is inductive. The oscillating frequency of the circuit is determined by this equivalent inductor in parallel with the combination of C1 and C2. As in the previous circuit, resistors R1, R2, and R3 provide the proper biasing conditions. The component labeled RFC is a radio-frequency choke that allows the direct current to be applied to the circuit while blocking the alternating signal.

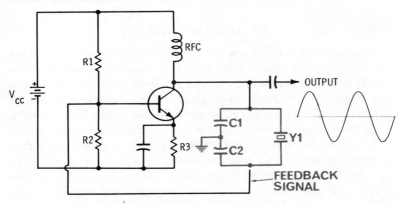

Fig. 5-13. Parallel crystal-controlled oscillator.

As the frequency of operation of both the LC and crystal-controlled oscillators gets lower, the size of the resonant components grows. Recall the formula relating frequency with L and C [$f = 1/(2\pi\sqrt{LC})$]. Quite often, at lower frequencies, other types of oscillators are used. Two of the more popular are the RC oscillator and the astable multivibrator, which will be covered in the next sections.

Q5-14. A crystal is a (high, low) impedance to a signal at its series-resonant frequency.

Q5-15. When operated in the parallel mode, the crystal acts like a (an) _____ and resonates with parallel capacitances of the circuit.

RC OSCILLATORS

The types of oscillators discussed in this section are called RC oscillators because the basic frequency-determining elements are resistors and capacitors. These types of oscillators are used in the audio-frequency range where bulky and expensive inductors may be undesirable. They can cover a wide frequency range, deliver a relatively constant amplitude signal with low distortion, and they have good frequency stability. The most common types of RC oscillators are the Wein bridge, the parallel-T network, and the phase shift. The one considered in this section is the phase shift, or ladder network, as it is sometimes called.

Phase-Shift Oscillator

Recall that the essential role of the feedback circuit is to provide a voltage that is of the right phase and magnitude to sustain oscillation. Inductors and capacitors provided this signal in the types of oscillators discussed previously. In the so-called phase-shift oscillator, resistor-capacitor circuits provide the required feedback signal necessary to sustain oscillations.

RC Network—The basic RC network used in the feedback path of phase-shift oscillators is shown in Fig. 5-14. If an a-c voltage is applied to such a circuit, the relationship between the magnitude of the capacitive reactance and the resistor will determine the phase relationship between the input and output signals. If the reactance of the capacitor [determined by $X_c = 1/(2\pi fC)$] is very small with respect to the resistor value, no significant phase shift will occur. This is the case for a coupling capacitor as used in the ordinary amplifier.

146

If the reactance of the capacitor is very large with respect to the resistor value, the output voltage will lead the input voltage by 90 degrees. The same type of reasoning applies if the capacitor were considered fixed and the resistor value changed. That is, a large resistor value, compared to the reactance of the capacitor, would result in no phase shift, while a very small resistor would result in a 90-degree phase shift.

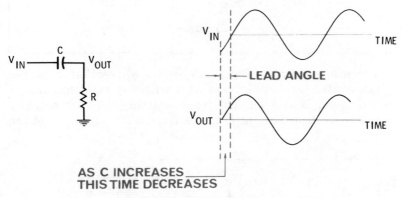

Fig. 5-14. RC network.

It might be useful to work one example in finding the reactance of a capacitor. Say we want to know the reactance of a 1-microfarad capacitor to a 1-kilohertz signal. Note that

$$\mathbf{X}_c = \frac{1}{2\pi fC} = \frac{1}{6.28 \times 1 \times 10^3 \times 1 \times 10^{-6}}$$
$$= .159 \times 10^3 = 159 \text{ ohms}$$

the reactance varies inversely with respect to the capacitor value and the frequency.

Q5-16. What does the phase shift between V_{in} and V_{out} in Fig. 5-14 depend on?

Q5-17. The reactance of a 1.5-microfarad capacitor at 5 kilohertz is _____.

Circuit Example—Fig. 5-15 shows an oscillator of the phase-shift type. Oscillations start with any random noise or when power is applied. The phase-shifting network actually consists of three RC sections. C1 R1, C2 R2, and C3 and the

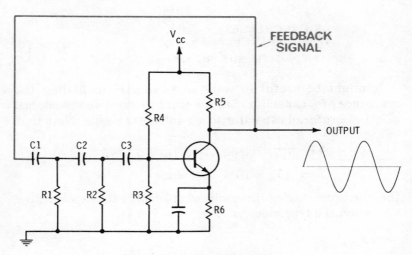

Fig. 5-15. Phase-shift oscillator.

parallel combination of R3,R4 and the input resistance to the transistor constitute the three sections. The signal at the collector of the transistor is 180 degrees out of phase with the signal at the base. That means that the phase-shift circuits must provide for an additional 180 degrees of

148

phase shift. Three sections are shown in the phase-shift network, so each section contributes 60 degrees of phase shift.

The output frequency is determined by this three-section phase-shifting network. This is because at only one frequency will the phase shift be 180 degrees. At other frequencies, the capacitive reactance is different and phase shifts other than 180 degrees occur. The feedback signal is not of the required phase then, and sustained oscillations will not occur.

The reader might ask why two sections with a 90-degree phase shift in each section could not be used. In order to achieve a 90-degree phase shift the capacitor would have to exhibit a large reactance with respect to the resistor, and this would attenuate the signal drastically. Even with a three-section phase-shifting network there is a considerable loss through the network and a high-gain transistor has to be used. Increasing the number of sections causes a reduction in the loss of the overall network but, of course, it means more components are needed. The usual phase-shift oscillator uses three sections as a compromise between the number of components and the gain required for the transistor.

The phase-shift oscillator can be made a variable-frequency oscillator by providing ganged capacitors or resistors in the phase-shift network. By changing the capacitors or resistors, the frequency at which there is a 180-degree phase shift will change, and therefore the frequancy of oscillation will change.

Q5-18. In reference to Fig. 5-15, if four RC sections were used in the phase-shift network, each section would contribute _____ degrees to the over-all required phase shift of _____ degrees.

Q5-19. The phase-shift oscillator is used mainly in the _____-frequency range.

RELAXATION OSCILLATORS

In general, relaxation oscillators are circuits in which one or more voltages change abruptly and periodically, thus producing a square-wave output. The period of the oscillations usually depends on the charge or discharge time constant of an RC circuit. Two of the more commonly used relaxation oscillator circuits are the astable multivibrator and the blocking oscillator. The circuit to be described in this chapter is the astable multivibrator.

Multivibrators

There are three types of multivibrators: the bistable, the monostable, and the astable. The bistable is a circuit in which either of the two transistors can remain on or off and stay in that state until a triggering pulse triggers the circuit. This condition is called a stable condition, and the prefix "bi" means two. Thus the word bistable means that the circuit is capable of being stable in either of two states (one transistor on and the other off, or vice versa).

The monostable multivibrator has only one stable state. This means that in the absence of any triggers, the same transistor is always on and the other one always off. In the presence of a trigger, they switch, but then revert to the stable state after a time determined by an RC time constant in the circuit.

The astable multivibrator is a circuit in which neither transistor reaches a stable state. When one is on, the other is off, and they continually switch back and forth at a rate depending on the RC time constants in the circuit.

RC Time Constants

To follow the operation of the astable multivibrator, it is necessary to understand the basic RC network. Fig. 5-16 shows a capacitor being charged to a voltage V through a resistor R. Before the switch is closed, the capacitor has no charge and therefore there is no voltage across it. When the switch is closed, the voltage on the capacitor cannot charge instantaneously to V, but takes a certain time to reach this voltage. This time is determined by the values of R and C.

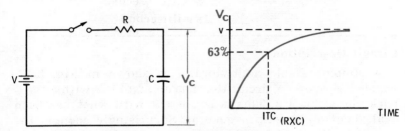

Fig. 5-16. Basic RC network.

The illustration shows a general plot of the voltage across the capacitor as a function of time. The product of R times C is called the time constant and is the number of seconds required for the capacitor to reach 63 percent of its full charge. Thus, for a 1000-ohm resistor and 1-mfd capacitor it would take .001 second (one time constant) for the capacitor to reach 63 percent of its full charge. A general rule of thumb is that for all practical purposes, the capacitor is fully charged after five time constants. This basic concept of time constant is used over and over again in pulse circuits.

Q5-20. Since the prefix *a* can mean "not" or "without," the _____ multivibrator is the one that never attains a stable state.

Q5-21. The value in milliseconds of the time constant for a 1500-ohm resistor and .12-mfd capacitor is _____ .

Circuit Description

A simple astable multivibrator is shown in Fig. 5-17. Fig. 5-17A shows a circuit that has an amplifier with a feedback signal via C2. This is consistent with what has been said about oscillators in general. Surprisingly enough, the circuit in Fig. 5-17B is the same one as in Fig. 5-17A, only

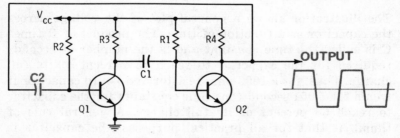

(A) Amplifier with feedback signal.

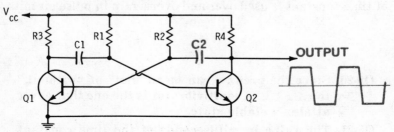

(B) Redrawn version of the same circuit.

Fig. 5-17. Simple astable multivibrator.

redrawn to show the symmetry of the astable multivibrator. It is easier to explain the operation of the circuit using Fig. 5-17B, but it is interesting to note from Fig. 5-17A that the circuit is an oscillator, operating on the same principles as the ones previously described.

The operation of the circuit can be explained as follows: Although the circuit is symmetrical, when power is first applied to the circuit one transistor conducts more than the other, due to some differences that are inevitable. Assume that Q1 conducts first. Then Q2 is off and its collector is at V_{cc}. This means that C2 is charged to a voltage nearly equal to V_{cc}. As C1 starts to charge toward V_{cc} through R1, a point will be reached where Q2 will be forward biased and Q2 will rapidly turn on. The collector voltage of Q2 will then drop and this negative going transition is coupled through C2 to the base of Q1, turning it off. Q1 will stay off until the charge on C2 is sufficient to turn it on. When Q1 turns on, its collector voltage drops from approximately V_{cc} to ground. This transition is coupled through C1 to the base of Q2, turning it off. Q2 will now stay off until C1 is charged enough through R1 to turn it on. This process of transferring the collector transitions through the capacitors to the opposite base continues periodically. The rate depends on the R1C1 and R2C2 time constants. These time constants determine how long it takes for the bases to become forward biased and initiate the switching action.

Note that the voltages at the collectors change abruptly. This square-wave output is characteristic of relaxation oscillators, as opposed to the nearly sinusoidal outputs of the other oscillators discussed previously.

Q5-22. **Referring to the astable multivibrator in Fig. 5-17, identify the two time constants that determine the period of the output waveform.**

Q5-23. **In a general way, the astable multivibrator (does, does not) operate on the same feedback principles as the sinusoidal oscillators.**

SUMMARY QUESTIONS

1. Oscillators are a necessary component in practically all large electronic systems. They are used extensively in the communications field in both transmitters and receivers. Digital computers use oscillators to establish time references. Many pieces of test equipment such as signal generators and pulse generators use oscillators. Because of their many uses and the wide range of frequencies covered, a number of different types of oscillator circuits are available.

   The general principles of operation apply to all the oscillators covered in this chapter. Feedback of the proper phase (positive feedback) and amplitude has to be supplied. The feedback has to supply enough signal to sustain the oscillations. This feedback is supplied in a number of different ways, depending on the type of oscillator. Quite often, the frequency-determining components of the circuit are part of the feedback loop. The three types of sinusoidal oscillators covered are the LC, crystal-controlled and the RC phase-shift types. The relaxation oscillator described is the astable multivibrator.

   a. Since the _____ of a sine wave determines the time of each cycle, an oscillator with good frequency stability makes a good master clock.

   b. If the feedback signal is of such a phase, with respect to the output, that it tends to produce an even larger amplitude output, it is known as _____ feedback.

2. The names commonly used for the three types of sinusoidal oscillators virtually describe the frequency de-

termining elements for each. The LC oscillator contains an LC tank circuit from which the feedback signal is derived. Such oscillators are generally used in the r-f frequency range. The crystal-controlled oscillator is used when a high degree of frequency stability is required. The crystal can be used as part of the actual tuned circuit, or it can be placed in the feedback path. In either event, the crystal determines the frequency of oscillation. The RC phase-shift oscillator uses RC sections in the feedback path to determine the frequency of oscillation. It is used in the audio frequency range.

a. In the phase-shift oscillator described in this chapter, the RC networks have to provide a total phase shift of _____ degrees.

b. The interaction of mechanical vibrations and voltage generation exhibited by crystals is known as the _____ effect.

c. Would a phase-shift oscillator be more likely to be used at 1500 hertz or 10 megahertz?

3. The relaxation oscillator selected for discussion in this chapter was the astable multivibrator. Although it operates by making abrupt voltage changes, it still adheres to the basic feedback principles of the other oscillators. This oscillator is characterized by its square-wave output as opposed to the nearly sinusoidal output of the other oscillators discussed in this chapter.

a. The period of oscillation of the astable multivibrator is determined by a pair of _____ time constants in the circuit.

SUMMARY ANSWERS

1a. Since the **period** of a sine wave determines the time of each cycle, an oscillator with good frequency stability makes a good master clock.

1b. If the feedback signal is of such a phase, with respect to the output, that it tends to produce an even larger amplitude output, it is known as **positive** feedback.

2a. In the phase-shift oscillator described in the chapter, the RC networks have to provide a total phase shift of **180 degrees**.

2b. The interaction of mechanical vibrations and voltage generation exhibited by crystals is known as the **piezo-electric** effect.

2c. Since the phase-shift oscillator is used mainly in the audio frequency range, it is more likely to be used at **1500 hertz** than 10 megahertz.

3a. The period of oscillation of the astable multivibrator is determined by a pair of **RC** time constants in the circuit.

6

Special Devices

The components covered in this chapter are relatively new semiconductor devices. Just like the transistor, they are small in size, have become relatively inexpensive with new manufacturing techniques, and consume less power than their electron-tube counterparts. Each of these devices operates with voltages and currents that are compatible with other semiconductor devices. For these reasons, they are found extensively in electronic equipment, performing many useful functions. The four devices described are the zener diode, silicon controlled rectifier, unijunction transistor, and the field-effect transistor.

The discussion of each of the four components will include a brief explanation of the semiconductor physics involved, followed by a description of the basic voltage-current characteristics. Some simple but illustrative circuits will then be explained to give some insight as to how these devices are used. The intention here is to acquaint the reader with the fundamental principles and design characteristics, rather than to attempt to detail the many applications.

It should be pointed out that these devices are well past the experimental stage and are already found in many diverse pieces of military and commercial electronic systems.

ZENER DIODES

The zener diode derives its electrical characteristics from a reverse-biased P-N junction. Earlier in this book, in Chapter 2, the P-N junction was introduced and its properties discussed in detail. At that time, the main interest was studying the P-N junction with the idea of extending the explanation to the transistor. For this reason, when the junction was forward biased we said there was current, and when the junction was reverse biased, we said there was no current. This latter statement is not completely true. Under certain conditions there is a small current due to minority carriers. This will now be explained.

Zener-Diode Theory

A brief review of the P-N junction is in order before describing the phenomenon that is characteristic of the zener diode. Recall that in a P-type semiconductor material, some of the semiconductor atoms have been replaced by an element that leaves the resultant material with positive charges (holes) diffused throughout it. This is shown in Fig. 6-1 as encircled plus signs in the P region. In a similar fashion, N-type material results when some of the atoms of the semiconductor material have been replaced by an element that leaves the material with the negatively charged electrons throughout. This is shown as encircled minus signs in the N region in Fig. 6-1.

A P-N junction results when an N-type region and a P-type region are formed in the same crystal. When a battery is connected to the junction as in Fig. 6-1A, the majority carriers are forced across the junction and there is current. When the battery is connected as in Fig. 6-1B, the majority carriers are forced away from the junction and there is no current. This is a simplified explanation of what happens. Actually, besides the positive majority carriers in the P-type material, there are always a few electrons. Likewise, there are positive holes in the N-type material as well as the electron majority carriers. For this reason, when the junction is reverse biased there is actually a small current due to these minority carriers just mentioned. This small current stays relatively constant until the potential of the reverse bias reaches a certain critical point at which break-down occurs, and so-called zener action takes place.

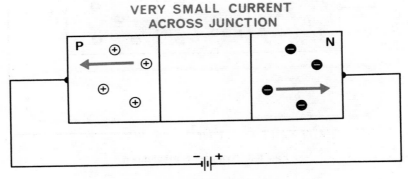

(A) *Forward bias.*

(B) *Reverse bias.*

Fig. 6-1. Diode biasing.

Q6-1. To reverse bias a P-N junction, the positive side of the battery is connected to the _____-type material and the negative side of the battery to the _____ type.

Q6-2. The minority carriers in N-type material are _____ and in P-type material are _____.

Breakdown Voltage—As the potential of the reverse voltage is increased, the electric field in the region of the junction also increases. When this field becomes sufficiently large, electrons could acquire enough energy so that upon collision with atoms they could remove valence electrons from their covalent bonds. These newly released electrons could in turn produce more carriers by collision. These

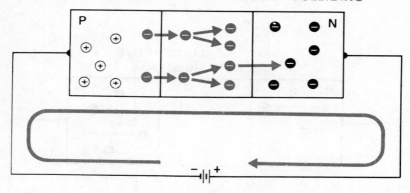

Fig. 6-2. Avalanche breakdown.

collisions continually increase the number of carriers across the junction and there is a relatively large reverse current. This process is called avalanche multiplication (Fig. 6-2). The series of events can also be initiated by the electric field itself breaking some covalent bonds and releasing electrons. The reverse voltage at which this avalanche phenomenon occurs is known as the zener breakdown voltage.

The interesting part of this process is that the diode will recover when the applied reverse voltage is reduced below the breakdown or zener value. No damage will occur unless the current is allowed to increase to the point where excessive heat is dissipated in the region of the junction.

Advantage is taken of this reverse-breakdown voltage of diodes to form a large family of so-called zener diodes. The reverse voltage at which the diode breaks down is closely related to the impurity concentration in the semiconductor. Thus, by regulating the amount of impurities, breakdown voltages from a few volts to hundreds of volts are available. The zener diodes, manufactured specifically to exhibit a certain reverse-breakdown characteristic, still behave as regular diodes in the forward direction. Zener diodes are used in a similar fashion as voltage regulator tubes, except that a much larger selection of voltages is available with the zener diodes.

It should be pointed out that practically all P-N junctions exhibit this zener breakdown phenomenon. It even occurs in the base to emitter and base to collector junctions of transistors. However, careful manufacturing processes are required to control the value of the zener breakdown voltage, which is the most important characteristic of the zener diode.

The voltage-current characteristic curve of the zener diode will be presented in the next section. This will enable the reader to gain more insight into how these devices are used in circuits.

Q6-3. The phenomenon that leads to a relatively large reverse current at the zener breakdown voltage is called _____ multiplication.

Q6-4. The zener diode is similar to a (regular diode, resistor) when it is forward biased.

Characteristic Curve

The voltage-current characteristic curve for a typical zener diode is shown in Fig. 6-3. The forward-biased zener is represented by the right-hand half of the curve and is similar to a regular semiconductor diode. The portion of the curve that characterizes the zener diode, and therefore, is of particular interest here, is the left-hand portion of the curve. The forward-voltage portion of the curve is not drawn in proportion to the reverse-voltage portion. The forward portion remains relatively constant for all zeners and it is drawn in the illustration out of proportion to the reverse voltage to show more detail. The position of the zener breakdown voltage will naturally vary, depending of the type of zener. This illustration shows a 15-volt zener diode.

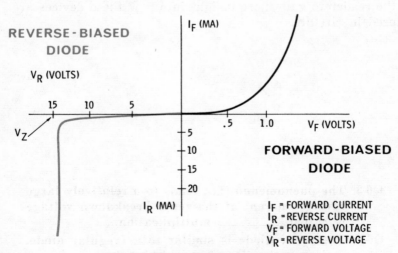

Fig. 6-3. Zener-diode characteristics.

The most important characteristic of the zener diode in selecting one for a particular application is the zener breakdown voltage. As the reverse voltage across the diodes is increased from zero, a point will be reached where the voltage will not increase any further. This point is labeled V_z in Fig. 6-3 and is called the zener breakdown voltage. At this point, the current changes from practically no conduction at all to a value that is determined by the amount of resistance in series with the zener diode. This is shown in Fig. 6-4. A power-supply voltage higher than the zener voltage should not be put directly across the zener because there will be nothing to limit the current, and destruction of the unit is likely to occur. The current through the zener is actually determined by the resistor in series with it, and the voltage across the two components. A simple calculation is included in the illustration to demonstrate the point.

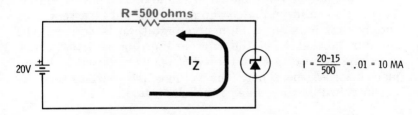

Fig. 6-4. Series-limiting resistor.

Of prime importance to notice in the illustration of Fig. 6-3 is that in the breakdown region, a constant voltage, V_z, is available for a rather large range of current. The limiting factor of the allowable amount of current that a zener can conduct is its rated maximum power dissipation as discussed in the next section, when some simple circuits are explained.

Q6-5. What determines the value of the zener breakdown voltage?

Q6-6. If the power supply in Fig. 6-4 were lowered to below _____ volts, there would be a negligible amount of current.

Basic Circuits

Probably the most basic circuit utilizing the zener diode is the regulator circuit shown in Fig. 6-5. The power source, V, could be an unregulated supply or it could be a regulated supply that puts out a higher voltage than is desired. The resistor labeled R is the current-limiting resistor which is in the circuit so that the whole power source V is not placed across the zener. The voltage delivered to load R_L is controlled by the value of the zener diode.

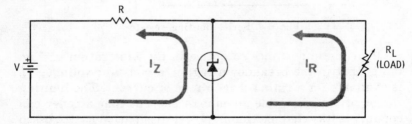

Fig. 6-5. Basic regulator circuit.

When load resistance R_L varies within certain limits, load current I_R will vary accordingly. However, the voltage across the load resistor will stay constant as fixed by the zener. Fig. 6-6 shows a generalized plot of how I_L, I_z and V_z vary as R_L varies. When R_L is zero (a short circuit), there is no current through the zener. As R_L is increased, the current through the zener remains zero until a value of voltage equal to the zener voltage is developed across R_L. The

164

zener then takes over and keeps the voltage across R_L constant for different values of R_L.

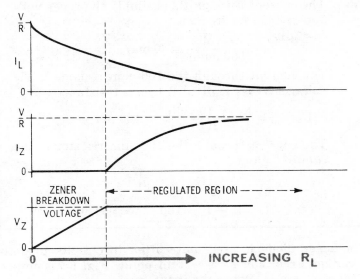

Fig. 6-6. Current-voltage relationship.

The power dissipated in the zener diode is simply the voltage across it times the current through it. The maximum current through the zener occurs when R_L is an open circuit. This would also be the maximum power-dissipation condition.

Q6-7. For the circuit shown what are the values of I_z and I_L?

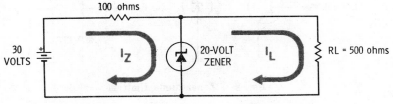

A6-7. The current through R_L is simply the zener voltage divided by R_L:

$$I_L = \frac{20 \text{ volts}}{500 \text{ ohms}} = \textbf{40 ma}$$

The current through the 100-ohm resistor is the voltage across it divided by its resistance:

$$I_{100 \text{ ohms}} = \frac{E_R}{I_R} = \frac{10 \text{ volts}}{100 \text{ ohms}} = 100 \text{ ma}$$

The current through the 100-ohm resistor is the sum of I_z and I_L:

$$I_R = I_z + I_L$$

or

$$I_z = I_R - I_L = 100 - 40 = \textbf{60 ma}$$

The zener diode is used quite often in circuits to limit the voltage excursion at a certain point. Fig. 6-7 shows a typical application. When the input level is a positive level, the transistor is turned on and the collector voltage is close to ground potential. When the input shifts to zero potential the transistor is turned off. If the zener diode was not in the circuit, the collector voltage would rise to V_{cc}, but with the zener in the circuit the collector voltage is limited to a value equal to V_z. One reason for doing this could be to limit the voltage from collector to emitter so that the V_{CE} rating of the transistor is not exceeded. Another reason could be to establish "logic levels" at zero and V_z.

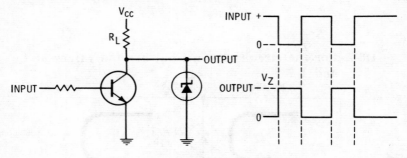

Fig. 6-7. Zener-diode limiter.

Another interesting application is the zener-diode clipper shown in Fig. 6-8. Two zeners are used back to back so that when the polarity of the input is such that one conducts as a zener, the other acts as a regular diode. If an alternating sine wave is applied to the input, a square wave will result

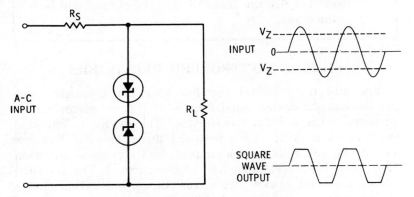

Fig. 6-8. Zener-diode clipper.

at the output. This assumes that the amplitude of the input signal is large enough so that the zeners will reach their breakdown potential. The zeners can be of the same value, in which case the square wave has equal positive and negative peaks. If the zeners are different values the positive and negative peaks of the square wave will be different accordingly.

Q6-8. The zener diode in the illustration of Fig. 6-8 limits the collector voltage to a value equal to _____.

Q6-9. If the amplitude of the input sine wave of the zener-diode clipper is too small to fire the zener diodes, will the output be a sine wave, a square wave, or zero output?

SILICON CONTROLLED RECTIFIERS

The silicon controlled rectifier (scr) is a multilayered semiconductor device consisting of 2 N-type materials alternated with 2 P-type materials. The device is called a rectifier because it has a forward direction that has low resistance and thus passes current, and a reverse direction that has a high resistance and blocks current. The forward direction is not always a low resistance, but rather under the control of a turn-on gate. The controlled rectifier is not always used to perform the usual rectifier functions. Applications making use of the controlling feature have been developed to make fullest use of its capabilities.

Silicon Controlled Rectifier Theory

The actual internal operation of the scr is somewhat involved and only a simplified explanation will be given. The basic internal construction is shown in Fig. 6-9A. The scr has three leads which are called the anode, the cathode, and the gate. The anode is attached to a P-type material which in turn forms the anode junction with an N-type material. These two layers are denoted by P_2 and N_1. The N_1 layer also forms a junction, called the control junction, with another layer of P-type material. This layer is labeled P_1 in the illustration, and has the gate lead attached to it. The P_1 layer in turn forms the so-called cathode junction with an N-type material which has the cathode attached to it.

The external signals are applied to the scr as shown in Fig. 6-9B. Because of the polarity of the external power supply connected between the anode and cathode, the anode and cathode junctions are forward biased, while the control junction is reversed biased. A positive trigger applied to the gate terminal will cause the cathode junction to pass current. The control junction can then be thought of as connected to the cathode through the low resistance of the cathode junction. The forward-biased anode junction then passes current and the whole device from anode to cathode is a low resistance and passes current easily. Note that before the positive trigger was applied to the gate, there was no current between the anode and cathode because of the reverse-biased control junction.

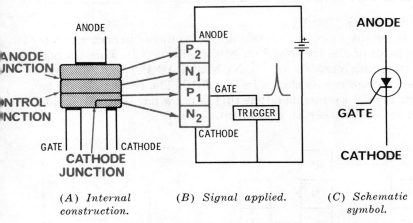

(A) *Internal construction.*   (B) *Signal applied.*   (C) *Schematic symbol.*

Fig. 6-9. Silicon controlled rectifier.

The schematic symbol for the scr is shown in Fig. 6-9C. It is very similar to a regular diode with the important addition of the gate lead that actually controls when the scr will pass current.

Q6-10. The scr is similar to a regular rectifier in that it has a (an) _____ and _____, but it also has an additional lead called the _____.

Q6-11. To initiate action in the scr and cause it to be forward biased, the positive side of the power supply is connected to the _____ and a positive trigger applied to the _____.

Scr Characteristics

It might help in describing the voltage-current characteristics of the scr to use an equivalent circuit. This equivalent circuit consists of an NPN and PNP transistor connected together as shown in Fig. 6-10. The reader should be cautioned to remember that this is not what is really inside an scr, but rather an equivalent circuit.

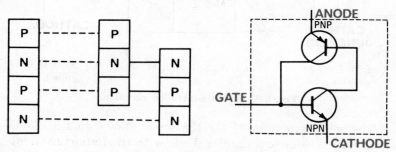

Fig. 6-10. Scr equivalent circuit.

Referring to the illustration, in the absence of any signal at the gate, both transistors are off, since the base current for each has to pass through the other transistor. Once a trigger is applied to the gate to turn the NPN transistor on, the PNP also conducts. This conduction will continue even after the gate trigger is removed. This is an important point. The trigger at the gate is necessary to initiate action, but once current starts between the anode and cathode, it will continue after the trigger has been removed. However, if the anode to cathode current is interrupted, the scr reverts to the blocking condition and has to be triggered again.

Fig. 6-11 shows a typical scr characteristic curve. If the anode to cathode is reverse biased, the device behaves similarly to a regular diode. In the forward-biased condition, there is very little current until the gate trigger is applied.

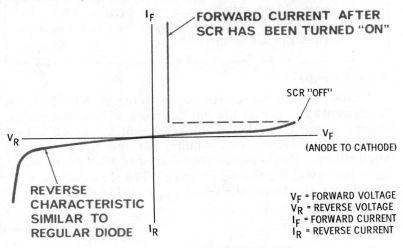

Fig. 6-11. Scr characteristic curve.

Note then how rapidly the forward current increases. This implies a need for a current-limiting resistor in series with the scr, just as the zener diode needed some current-limiting device when it fired. The forward characteristics actually consist of two conditions. The first condition is when the scr is off and there is very little current, and the second condition is when the scr is on and a relatively large current occurs and the voltage drop across the scr is small.

Q6-12. There are two distinct conditions possible when an scr is forward biased from anode to cathode. What determines which of these conditions the scr will actually be in at any given time?

171

Basic Circuits

A basic application of the scr is shown in Fig. 6-12. In this circuit the scr is placed in series with a relay coil. When switch S1 is closed, the relay will not be energized until the time-delay circuit supplies a trigger to the scr. One application of this is to allow the filaments of a tube to warm up before applying the high voltage. The time-delay circuit would then determine the warm-up period.

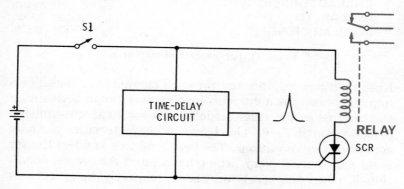

Fig. 6-12. Scr relay circuit.

An interesting application of the scr is the voltage-regulator circuit illustrated in Fig. 6-13. The circuit is not complete as drawn, but it does show the function of the scr's. SCR1, SCR2, CR1, and CR2 form a bridge-rectifier circuit. The box labeled SENSING AND TIMING CIRCUIT pulses the scr's so that the one that is forward biased by the a-c signal will be brought into conduction at the point in the a-c cycle which will give the desired d-c output. The output voltage is sensed by the sensing circuit which then applies a trigger to the gates of the scr's to cause the appropriate one to conduct at just the right time. If the output voltage is either too low or too high, the sensing circuit will apply the trigger to the scr at a time so that more or less of the input signal is delivered to the load.

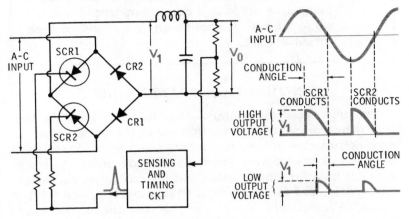

Fig. 6-13. Scr regulator.

The time that the scr's are on is called the *conduction angle*. Waveshapes illustrating the typical situation are also shown. The point to notice is that the sensing and timing circuit controls the conduction angle, which in turn will control the output voltage. In this particular application, the scr performs the function of a rectifier for a period of time determined by the output voltage.

Q6-13. The conduction angle for the scr's in Fig. 6-13 is regulated by the triggers from the sensing circuit. A small conduction angle will give a (low, high) output voltage while a large conduction angle will give a (low, high) output voltage.

173

UNIJUNCTION TRANSISTORS

The unijunction transistor derives its name from the fact that it has only one P-N junction—thus the prefix "uni." It does not operate in the same manner as regular transistors do, but rather performs functions that are unique to itself. It is not used for amplification, but because of its characteristics, it is used for oscillators, timing circuits, and trigger circuits. You should understand that the unijunction transistor performs only certain functions and does not really belong to the regular family of transistors.

Theory of Unijunction Transistors

Even though the unijunction transistor has only one P-N junction, it still has three leads. This is because two of the leads are connected to opposite ends of the same N-type material. This construction is shown in Fig. 6-14A. The two leads connected to the same material are called base 1 and base 2, while the third lead, which is connected to the P-type material, is called the emitter. The P-type material does not form a junction along the whole length of the N-type material, but instead, a small junction is formed close to the base 2 lead. The result of this construction will now be explained.

The power supply connected between base 2 and base 1 establishes a voltage gradient through the N-type material. If the potential in the N-type material, opposite to the location of the P-type material, is larger than the supply in the emitter circuit, the junction is reverse biased. If the voltage in the emitter circuit is increased, the junction will eventually become forward biased. Holes will then be injected from the P-type material into the N-type (just as in a conventional forward-biased diode) and will be swept toward base 1. This reduces the resistance between the emitter and base 1, and the current continues to increase, with its final value depending on the voltage supply in the emitter circuit. Current will also increase in the base circuits due to the action of the forward-biased junction.

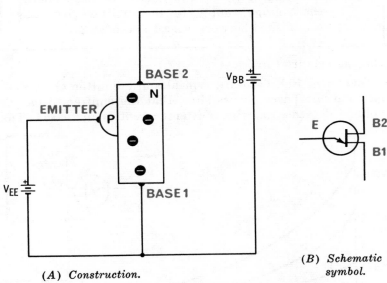

(A) Construction.

(B) Schematic symbol.

Fig. 6-14. Unijunction transistor.

The symbol for the unijunction transistor is shown in Fig. 6-14B. You might notice in the drawing that if base 1 and base 2 were connected directly together, the resultant device would be very similar to the conventional diode.

Q6-14. Even though the unijunction transistor has only _____ junction, it has _____ leads. Name the leads.

Q6-15. A voltage gradient that has to be overcome by the voltage supply in the emitter circuit is established between _____ and _____.

Characteristics Curves

Shown in Fig. 6-15 are typical static emitter characteristic curves. These curves show that the emitter to base 1 voltage decreases as the emitter current is increased. The

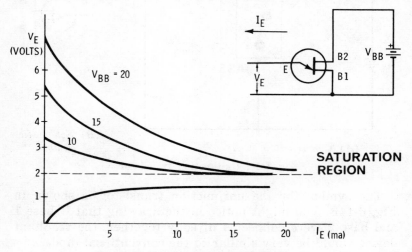

Fig. 6-15. Emitter characteristic curves.

peculiarity of having the voltage decrease while the current is increasing is called negative resistance. For a given V_{BB}, the curve shows what emitter voltage is required for various values of emitter currents. Note that as the emitter current gets larger than a certain value, the emitter voltage remains the same, regardless of the V_{BB} value. This is known as the saturation region.

Another useful curve is shown. This curve relates the emitter current with the base 2 current. Depending on the circuit configuration, it might be important to know the current in the base 2 lead as a function of the emitter current.

It should be noted that the curves are static curves. This means they are plotted as if all the parameters are d-c volt-

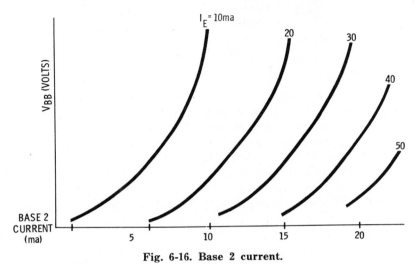

Fig. 6-16. Base 2 current.

ages and currents. In actual operation, V_{BB} is usually a d-c power supply, but V_E is usually a pulse or trigger derived by charging and discharging a capacitor. The curves do give some idea of what can be expected, and they can be used to compare one type of unijunction transistor with another.

Q6-16. As V_{BB} increases, the voltage at the emitter required to trigger the unijunction _____.

Q6-17. The phenomenon of having a voltage decrease while the current is increasing is called _____ resistance.

Basic Circuits

Probably the most basic and widely used circuit employing the unijunction transistor is that shown in Fig. 6-17. The circuit is a relaxation oscillator that can be used as a sawtooth or trigger generator. When power is first applied, capacitor C charges through R1. When the voltage across C is large enough, the unijunction fires and the capacitor discharges through the unijunction. When the capacitor discharges sufficiently, there is not enough emitter current and the unijunction shuts off. The capacitor starts to recharge and the cycle begins again. The result is a sawtooth waveform across the capacitor and a train of triggers at base 1. The triggers appear across R2 at the time the unijunction fires, and a current is developed in the emitter-base 1 circuit. The frequency of the sawtooth and triggers depends on the R1-C time constant. The usefulness of the unijunction transistor is that it does the work of two or three conventional transistors in the generation of a sawtooth or triggering waveshape.

Quite often the trigger at the base 1 lead is used to actuate an scr, as shown in Fig. 6-18. The unijunction acts as a time delay, since the trigger will not appear at base 1 until the capacitor is sufficiently charged. Thus the R1-C time

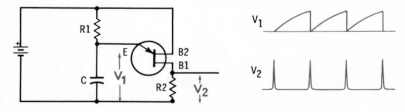

Fig. 6-17. Unijunction oscillator.

constant will determine the delay between the application
of power to the circuit and the time when the scr fires. The
relay is shown to indicate what type of load the scr might
be controlling. In actual operating circuits, a circuit is usu-

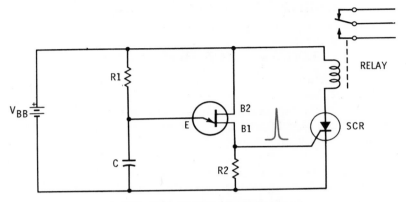

Fig. 6-18. Unijunction trigger.

ally incorporated that shuts off the unijunction after it has
turned the scr on so that it does not keep supplying triggers
to the gate of the scr. Recall that once an scr is turned on,
the gate signal can be removed and the scr will stay on.

Q6-18. The frequency of oscillation of a unijunction
transistor is usually controlled by a (an) _____
time constant in the emitter circuit.

FIELD-EFFECT TRANSISTORS

An important recent advancement in the semiconductor field is the field-effect transistor (fet). The basic principle on which these devices operate is the control of current by an electric field, whereas in a regular transistor one current is controlled by another current. One of the basic features of fet's is the very high input impedance, which implies that the input is voltage controlled much as the vacuum tube. As a matter of fact, the characteristics of an fet are similar enough to a vacuum tube so that engineers can adapt their vacuum-tube knowledge very readily to the fet. It is somewhat ironic that in order to study the transistor, one has always been told to forget about vacuum tubes and learn transistor theory from the beginning. Now there is a transistor that is more like a tube than like a regular transistor.

Fet Theory

There are two types of fet's, known as the junction field-effect transistor (jfet) and the insulated-gate field-effect transistor (igfet). Quite often, the igfet is called the "metal oxide semiconductor" field-effect transistor (mos fet), which is what it will be called in this book.

Jfet—Basically, a jfet can be considered as a variable resistor. This resistor is really a doped silicon bar that can be either an N-type or P-type material. Fig. 6-19A shows an N-type material. Two terminals are connected to this bar; one is called the source and the other is called the drain. Current between the source and drain depends on the resistance of the N-type material. A P-type region is diffused into the N-type bar. This P-type material is used to control the resistance of the N-type material, and so the lead attached to it is called the gate. As with all P-N junctions, a depletion region is formed around the junction. The size of the region depends on the amount of reverse voltage applied to the junction. As the reverse voltage is increased, the depletion region enlarges and spreads into the N-type material and restricts the current. The actual resistance of the N-type

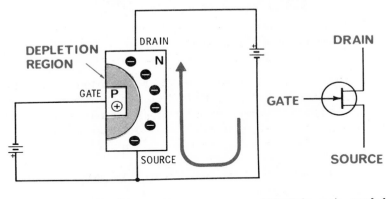

(A) Construction.   (B) Schematic symbol.

Fig. 6-19. N-channel jfet.

material between the source and drain is regulated by the size of the depletion region. This in turn is controlled by the reverse bias between gate and source. Note that there is no current in the gate circuit since the junction is reverse biased. Fig. 6-19B of the illustration shows the symbol for an N-channel jfet.

A P-channel fet can be formed by starting with a P-type bar between the source and drain and diffusing an N-type material for the gate. The word channel is used to indicate that current between the source and drain is channelized by the action of the depletion region.

Q6-19. In a jfet, current is between the terminals called the _____ and _____ under control of a field caused by a voltage applied to the _____.

Q6-20. The actual current restriction is a function of the size of the _____ region.

Mos fet—The insulated-gate fet, more often called the mos fet, operates with a different control mechanism than the jfet. The N-channel device is constructed as shown in Fig. 6-20A. Two N-type materials are diffused into a P-type substrate. These two N-type materials are the source and

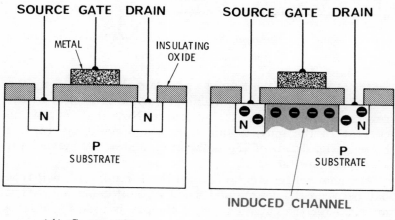

(A) *Construction.*   (B) *Drain-source current.*

Fig. 6-20. N-channel mos fet.

drain. An insulating oxide material covers the whole surface except for holes for the leads to the source and drain. The gate metal is then attached to the insulating oxide layer.

In the construction just described, there is no physical connection or junction between the gate and either the source or the drain. Thus, no current exists in the gate circuit and for all practical purposes the input gate can be considered an open circuit. The operation of the mos fet depends on the field created between the gate and substrate material to

182

induce current between the N-type materials forming the source and drain. As a positive voltage at the gate is increased, negative charges are induced in the vicinity of the substrate, between the source and drain. This causes the material in this region to become an N-type material. A so-called "channel" of N-type material is then formed between the source and drain, as shown in Fig. 6-20B and there is current in the drain-source circuit. This current will depend on how much of an N-type material is formed by the gate field. In other words, the drain-source current is regulated by the gate voltage.

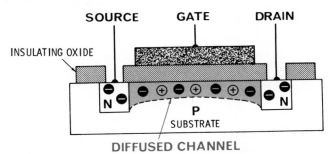

Fig. 6-21. Depletion-type mos fet.

The type of mos fet just described is an *enhancement* type because the gate voltage increases the number of carriers in the channel. Another type of mos fet is called a *depletion* type. In this device, a resistive N-type channel is diffused in the substrate between the source and drain, as shown in Fig. 6-21. The gate voltage decreases the carriers in this channel, thus decreasing the drain-source current. The operations of these two types will become clearer in the next section, in which the characteristic curves are covered.

Q6-21. In an enhancement-type mos fet, the gate voltage (increases, decreases) the number of current carriers in the channel.

Characteristic Curves

Transfer Curves—Typical transfer curves for N-channel devices are shown in Fig. 6-22. These curves show the cur-

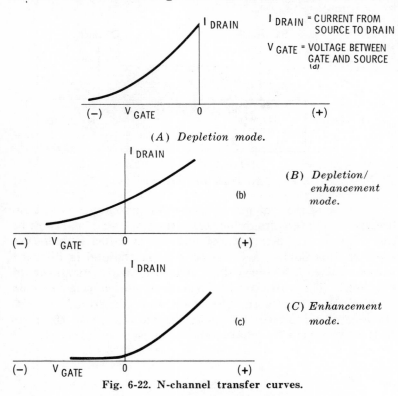

I DRAIN = CURRENT FROM SOURCE TO DRAIN

V GATE = VOLTAGE BETWEEN GATE AND SOURCE

(*A*) *Depletion mode.*

(*B*) *Depletion/ enhancement mode.*

(*C*) *Enhancement mode.*

Fig. 6-22. N-channel transfer curves.

rent-voltage relationships for the depletion and enhancement modes just described, as well as a combination of them called the depletion/enhancement mode. These curves, and the whole discussion of most fet's, has been based on the N-channel device. P-channel devices are made by switching the N-type materials for P-type and vice versa. The polarities of applied voltages would have to be reversed, also. This is the same situation as with NPN and PNP transistors. The symbols for the P-channel and N-channel types are shown in Fig 6-23.

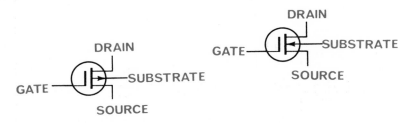

(A) P channel.   (B) N channel.

Fig. 6-23. Mos fet symbols.

The current-voltage transfer curves shown in Fig. 6-22 indicate what the depletion and enhancement modes mean in terms of gate voltage and drain current. For the depletion mode, at zero gate voltage there is a certain amount of drain current. As the gate voltage is decreased the current is reduced. In the enhancement type, at zero gate voltage the drain current is zero. The gate voltage is increased to increase the drain current. The depletion/enhancement mode is a combination of the two. At zero gate volts, there is drain current and it can be increased or decreased from this value by increasing or decreasing the gate voltage. The output characteristic curves of the next section will help to relate this information to circuit applications.

Q6-22. With zero volts between gate and source, which of the three modes will have zero drain current?

Q6-23. Draw the symbols for both the P-channel and N-channel mos fet and label the leads.

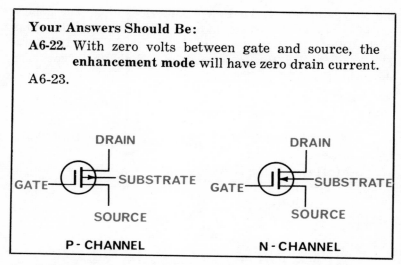

P - CHANNEL   **N - CHANNEL**

Output Characteristic Curves

Typical output characteristic curves for the three modes of mos fet operation are illustrated in Fig. 6-24. Again the N-channel device is chosen for illustration. Note how the characteristics are similar to a pentode tube. The shape is similar to transistor curves but there is a very important difference in that the running variable for the transistor is base *current* while the running variable for mos fet's is gate *voltage.*

The design of a circuit follows pretty much the same procedure as for a transistor. A load line is determined and a quiescent point selected. For linear amplification, the quiescent point is chosen to be in the center of the curves so that the operating point can move up and down the load line in the linear region. The mos fet can also be used as a switching device, in which case gate voltages are applied which will either turn the fet on into saturation, or off into the cut-off region.

The values for the different parameters give only an indication of the magnitudes of the voltages and currents involved. Since there are three modes, quite a bit of versatility is available. Usually, the requirements of the circuit to be used will dictate which mode and type of mos fet is to be used.

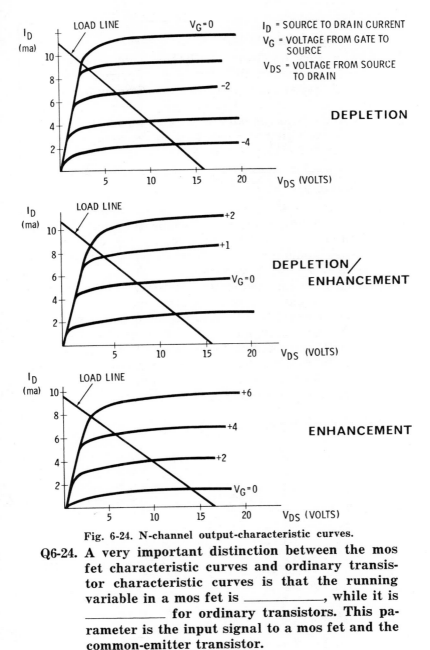

Fig. 6-24. N-channel output-characteristic curves.

Q6-24. A very important distinction between the mos fet characteristic curves and ordinary transistor characteristic curves is that the running variable in a mos fet is _____, while it is _____ for ordinary transistors. This parameter is the input signal to a mos fet and the common-emitter transistor.

Basic Circuits

Just as with transistors, there is an unlimited number of circuits that could utilize the fet. Applications include audio, rf, switching, logic, and timing circuits. Fig. 6-25 shows a simple, basic audio amplifier. Resistors R1 and R2 establish the quiescent-point voltage at the gate. The a-c signal to be amplified is superimposed on the gate bias, and the amplified output signal is taken from the drain terminal.

A switching circuit is shown in Fig. 6-26. This circuit uses both an N-channel fet and a P-channel fet. As the input signal switches from zero to V volts the output switches from V volts to zero, thus performing a simple inversion function. Fet's are found in more and more computers, performing all the required logical functions.

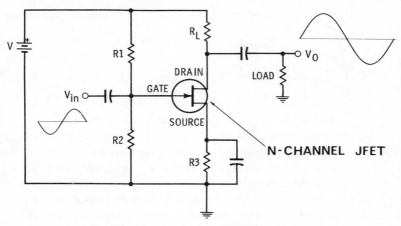

Fig. 6-25. Typical jfet amplifier circuit.

The two circuits mentioned are intended to show how an fet is connected in a circuit. The range of applications of fet's broadens continuously. Since it has a very high input impedance, the fet is ideally suited for audio and instrumen-

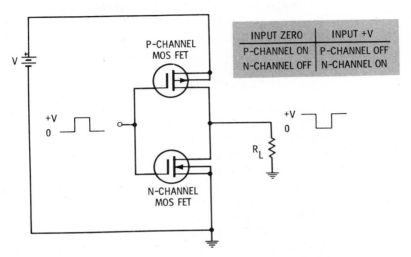

INPUT ZERO	INPUT +V
P-CHANNEL ON	P-CHANNEL OFF
N-CHANNEL OFF	N-CHANNEL ON

Fig. 6-26. Complementary circuit using mos fet's.

tation applications where the junction transistor is not too successful. The high input impedance also allows timing circuits with very long time constants to be designed in the gate circuit. The fet is not capable of handling large powers as are some of the power junction transistors, nor is it capable of very high frequency operation as are some of the junction transistors. However, it is finding its way into more equipment as new manufacturing techniques allow its price to be competitive with other devices.

Q6-25. Many of the applications of the fet make use of its very _____ input impedance.

Q6-26. Name two limitations of the fet as compared to the regular junction transistor.

SUMMARY QUESTIONS

1. The four special devices discussed in this chapter are the zener diode, silicon controlled rectifier, unijunction transistor, and the field-effect transistor.

   a. Draw the symbol and label the leads for each of the following devices; zener diode, silicon controlled rectifier, unijunction transistor, and the N-channel junction field-effect transistor.

2. The zener diode is a P-N junction device that is specially manufactured for its reverse-bias characteristics. When the reverse-bias voltage reaches the breakdown point, the diode will maintain this voltage. For this reason, one of the main uses of the zener diode is as a voltage regulator. It is also used in many applications as a protective device.

   a. The zener diode exhibits a constant _____ when it reaches the breakdown region.

   b. What is the value of the current through R_L for the circuit shown?

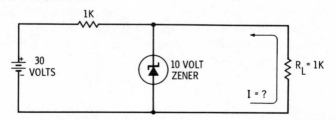

3. The silicon controlled rectifier is a multijunction device. It is a rectifier in the sense that it will pass current readily in only one direction. Its ability to switch to the conducting mode from the blocked condition is controlled by a gate signal. The gate has to be triggered only once be-

cause when the device has been activated, it stays that way until anode current is interrupted.

   a. The silicon controlled rectifier will stay in the conducting mode (anode current) even though the _____ signal is removed.

   b. The silicon controlled rectifier will assume the blocked condition when the _____ current is interrupted.

4. The unijunction transistor consists of a single P-N junction. However, it has a lead attached to each end of the N-type material. The input is applied to the lead connected to the P-type material, called the emitter. When this voltage reaches a certain level, the unijunction fires and exhibits a negative-resistance characteristic. This gives it the capability to be used as a relaxation oscillator.

   a. The unijunction transistor fires when the amplitude of the trigger applied between the _____ and _____ is large enough to forward bias that junction.

   b. In its most common application, the unijunction is used as a relaxation oscillator whose frequency of operation depends on a (an) _____ time constant in the emitter circuit.

5. There are basically two types of field-effect transistors. They are the junction type and the insulated-gate type. Both types have similar characteristics, but the internal mechanisms are different. The characteristics of the fet are much like those of a pentode vacuum tube. Probably the most distinguishing feature of the fet is its very high input impedance.

   a. Whereas the ordinary junction transistor is a current-controlled device, the fet is controlled by an electric _____ supplied by the gate circuit.

   b. Draw the symbol for an N-channel mos fet, labeling all the leads.

   c. The characteristics of a mos fet resemble closely the characteristics of a _____ vacuum tube.

SUMMARY ANSWERS

1a.

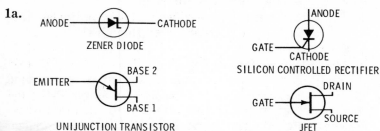

2a. The zener diode exhibits a constant **voltage** when it reaches the breakdown region.

2b.

$$I = \frac{E}{R_L}$$

$R_L = 1000$ ohms

$E = $ Value of zener breakdown voltage $= 10$ volts

Therefore $I = \dfrac{E}{R} = \dfrac{10 \text{ volts}}{1000 \text{ ohms}} = \mathbf{10}$ **milliamps.**

3a. The silicon controlled rectifier will stay in the conducting mode (anode current) even though the **gate** signal is removed.

3b. The silicon controlled rectifier will assume the blocked condition when the **anode** current is interrupted.

4a. The unijunction fires when the amplitude of the trigger applied between the **emitter** and **base 1** is large enough to forward bias that junction.

4b. In its most common application, the unijunction is used as a relaxation oscillator whose frequency of operation depends on an **RC** time constant in the emitter circuit.

5a. Whereas the ordinary junction transistor is a current-controlled device, the fet is controlled by an electric **field** supplied by the gate circuit.

5b.

DRAIN

GATE—[]—**SUBSTRATE**

SOURCE

5c. The characteristics of a mos fet resemble closely the characteristics of a **pentode** vacuum tube.

1. The basic function of a transistor in a circuit is to control or regulate current supplied by the _____ into the desired voltage or current signal.

    a. load
    b. amplifier
    c. power supply
    d. collector

2. Electrons flow away from the _____ terminal of the power supply toward the _____ terminal.

    a. negative, positive
    b. forward, reverse
    c. emitter, collector
    d. positive, negative

3. _____ are negatively charged particles that whirl in discrete orbits around the centrally located _____ of the atom.

    a. Protons, base
    b. Electrons, nucleus
    c. Protons, nucleus
    d. Electrons, proton

4. Normally, there are as many electrons as there are _____ in a given atom, which leaves the entire atom electrically _____.

    a. ions, negative
    b. orbits, charged
    c. neutrons, neutral
    d. protons, neutral

5. The electrons in the outer shell of an atom, which determine the electrical and chemical properties of a material, are called _____ electrons.

    a. excess
    b. valence
    c. recombined
    d. positive

6. Silicon and germanium are _____ materials commonly used for transistors.

    a. conductive
    b. insulator
    c. semiconductive
    d. translucent

7. Semiconductor materials are made useful for transistors by adding _____ elements such as gallium, indium or arsenic.

    a. N-type
    b. P-type
    c. gaseous
    d. impurity

8. To form a P-type material, indium atoms could be substituted for some germanium atoms. The resultant bonds would result in the generation of _____, which would leave the material with a net _____ charge.

    a. protons, positive
    b. holes, negative
    c. holes, positive
    d. electrons, negative

9. Majority carriers in N-type materials are _____, while in P-type materials _____ are the majority carriers.

    a. electrons, protons
    b. holes, electrons
    c. electrons, donors
    d. electrons, holes

10. If the positive terminal of a battery is connected to the N region of a P-N junction and the negative terminal is connected to the P region, the junction is _____ biased.

    a. forward
    b. reverse
    c. positively
    d. self

11. In normal operation, the reversed-biased transistor junction is the _____ to _____, while the forward-biased junction is the _____ to _____.

    a. collector to emitter, collector to base
    b. collector to base, collector to emitter
    c. base to collector, base to emitter
    d. base to emitter, base to collector

12. Two types of transistors, classified by the arrangement of the N- and P-type materials, are the _____ and _____.

    a. NPN, PNP
    b. NPN, PPN
    c. NPN, PNN
    d. NNP, PNP

13. The three regions comprising the transistor are called the _____, _____, and _____.

    a. emitter, base, anode
    b. base, collector, gate
    c. collector, base, emitter
    d. collector, base, cathode

14. The sum of base and collector current is _____ current.

    a. load
    b. bias
    c. input
    d. emitter

15. The circuit shown in the figure is a common-_____ circuit.

    a. emitter
    b. collector
    c. base
    d. none of the above

16. The common-emitter circuit is so called because the _____ is common to both the _____ signal and _____ signal.

    a. emitter, input, output
    b. collector, output, load
    c. emitter, a-c, d-c
    d. base, input, output

17. The common-collector circuit is also popularly known as a grounded _____ or a(n) _____ follower.

    a. collector, electron
    b. collector, cathode
    c. emitter, collector
    d. collector, emitter

18. The output signal in the common-base configuration is taken between the _____ and _____.

    a. collector, emitter
    b. collector, base
    c. base, emitter
    d. emitter, base

19. Biasing circuits determine the _____ point, which is the operating condition before a signal is applied.

    a. quiescent
    b. frequency cutoff
    c. recombination
    d. saturation

20. For the common-emitter circuit, the load line drawn on

the output characteristic curves connects two points. One point is the value of ____ ____ current when the full V_{CC} is across the load resistor.

a. base
b. collector
c. input signal
d. output signal

21. The second point that determines the load line is the value of _____ when the full V_{CC} is across the transistor from collector to emitter.

a. output voltage
b. base current
c. V_{BE}
d. V_{CE}

22. In the common-emitter circuit, the common-emitter current gain, collector current, and base current are related by the equation $I_c =$ _____.

a. βI_b
b. αI_b
c. $I_b + I_e$
d. $\beta + I_b$

23. In the common-base circuit, the common-base current gain, emitter current, and collector current are related by the equation $I_c =$ _____.

a. βI_e
b. $\alpha + I_e$
c. αI_e
d. αI_b

24. The common _____ configuration is the most commonly used of the three circuits because of its versatility in giving both current and voltage gain.

a. emitter
b. base
c. collector
d. input

25. The common _____ configuration gives _____ amplification, and the output signal is in phase with the input signal.

a. collector, voltage
b. emitter, current
c. base, current
d. collector, current

26. For a class-A amplifier, the biasing circuit is designed so that the quiescent point is _____ of the characteristic curves.

a. in the middle of the linear region
b. is near the cutoff region
c. is near the saturation region
d. on the zero base current line

27. In the _____ amplifier, the transistor bias and amplitude of the input signal are such that the transistor conducts current for appreciably _____ than one half of each cycle of the input signal.

a. class-A, less
b. class-C, less
c. class-B, more
d. class-C, more

28. The part of a circuit that establishes the desired collector operating point is called the _____ circuit.

a. biasing
b. feedback
c. output
d. tuned

29. The _____ circuit consists of two transistors; one conducts during one half of the

input signal and the other conducts during the other half.

a. tuned
b. RC
c. push-pull
d. phase-shift

30. A peaking coil is added in series with the _____ in the collector circuit of an RC amplifier to form a type of video amplifier called the _____-peaked amplifier.

a. resistor, series
b. resistor, positive
c. power supply, series
d. resistor, shunt

31. An essential ingredient in a sine-wave oscillator is _____.

a. 90-degrees phase shift
b. positive feedback
c. negative feedback
d. NPN transistors

32. The _____ type oscillator produces a square-wave output because the transistors actually act as switches, turning on and off.

a. RC
b. crystal
c. LC
d. relaxation

33. An important equation relating the resonant frequency of a tuned circuit with the values of the inductor and capacitor is _____.

a. $f = 2\pi \sqrt{LC}$

b. $f = \dfrac{1}{2\pi \sqrt{LC}}$

c. $f = \dfrac{1}{2\pi LC}$

d. $f = \dfrac{LC}{2\pi}$

34. In broad terms, an oscillator could be thought of as an amplifier that has enough _____ _____ applied to it so that it sustains oscillations.

a. base bias
b. negative feedback
c. positive feedback
d. input signal

35. If a mechanical force is applied to certain types of crystals, a voltage is generated and vice versa. This is known as the _____ effect which is utilized in crystal oscillators.

a. piezoelectric
b. electron-recombination
c. voltage-generating
d. positive-feedback

36. The most frequency-stable oscillator mentioned in this book is the _____ oscillator.

a. crystal
b. relaxation
c. phase shift
d. LC

37. In the Wien bridge and phase-shift type of oscillators, _____ circuits are the frequency-determining components.

a. harmonic crystal
b. capacitor-inductor
c. inductor-resistor
d. resistor-capacitor

38. If three RC sections are used in an RC oscillator to provide the feedback signal, each section should contribute approximately _____ degrees of the total phase shift.

a. 90
b. 45
c. 180
d. 60

39. The type of relaxation oscillator described in this book is the _____ multivibrator.

   a. one-shot
   b. monostable
   c. bistable
   d. astable

40. The astable multivibrator depends on two _____ time constants to determine its frequency of oscillation.

   a. RC
   b. LC
   c. transistor
   d. short

41. The _____ diode makes use of the phenomenon of _____ multiplication that produces a large current when the diode is sufficiently reverse biased.

   a. reverse, current
   b. zener, avalanche
   c. emitter, avalanche
   d. zener, electron

42. In its breakdown region, the zener diode exhibits a constant _____ characteristic.

   a. current
   b. voltage
   c. gain
   d. amplification

43. To operate the zener diode as a regulator, the more positive voltage is applied to the _____, and the more negative voltage to the _____.

   a. cathode, gate
   b. anode, cathode
   c. gate, cathode
   d. cathode, anode

44. To initiate action in the scr and cause it to be forward biased, the positive side of the power supply is connected to the _____ and a positive trigger applied to the _____.

   a. anode, gate
   b. anode, base
   c. cathode, gate
   d. anode, cathode

45. The scr is similar to a regular _____ with the important addition of the _____ signal, which actually controls when the scr will pass current.

   a. transistor, base
   b. diode, gate
   c. diode, anode
   d. diode, cathode

46. The unijunction has only one P-N junction and works on the principle that the voltage at the _____ has to overcome the voltage gradient established between the two _____.

   a. drain, emitter
   b. emitter, bases
   c. bases, emitter
   d. gate, bases

47. As the voltage between base 1 and base 2 of a ujt increases, it follows that the voltage at the emitter required to trigger the device _____.

   a. decreases
   b. remains the same
   c. increases
   d. slightly decreases

48. The frequency of oscillation of a ujt oscillator is usually controlled by an _____ time constant in the _____ circuit.

   a. RC, base 1
   b. RC, emitter

c. LC, emitter
d. RC, base 2

49. In a junction fet, there is current between the terminals called the _____ and _____ under the control of a field caused by a voltage applied to the _____.

    a. gate, source, drain
    b. collector, emitter, base

c. drain, gate, source
d. source, drain, gate

50. The three leads of the mos fet are called the _____, _____ and _____.

    a. gate, drain, source
    b. emitter, gate, source
    c. base, drain, source
    d. gate, drain, collector

ANSWERS TO FINAL TEST

1.	c.	18.	b.	35.	a.
2.	a.	19.	a.	36.	a.
3.	b.	20.	b.	37.	d.
4.	d.	21.	d.	38.	d.
5.	b.	22.	a.	39.	d.
6.	c.	23.	c.	40.	a.
7.	d.	24.	a.	41.	b.
8.	c.	25.	d.	42.	b.
9.	d.	26.	a.	43.	d.
10.	b.	27.	b.	44.	a.
11.	c.	28.	a.	45.	b.
12.	a.	29.	c.	46.	b.
13.	c.	30.	d.	47.	c.
14.	d.	31.	b.	48.	b.
15.	b.	32.	d.	49.	d.
16.	a.	33.	b.	50.	a.
17.	d.	34.	c.		

Index

A

B

C